S0-AWU-400

Eureka Math
Grade 1
Module 1

Special thanks go to the Gordon A. Cain Center and to the Department of Mathematics at Louisiana State University for their support in the development of *Eureka Math*.

For a free *Eureka Math* Teacher Resource Pack, Parent Tip Sheets, and more please visit www.Eureka.tools

Printed in the U.S.A.

This book may be purchased from the publisher at eureka-math.org

10 9 8 7 6

ISBN 978-1-63255-288-4

Name _____   Date _____

Circle 5, and then make a number bond.

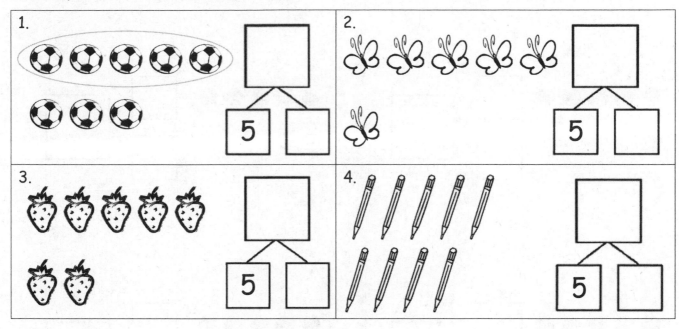

Put nail polish on the number of fingernails shown from left to right. Then, fill in the parts. Make the number of fingernails on one hand a part.

5.

8

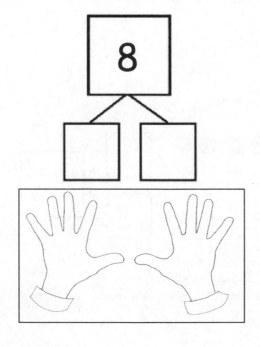

6.

6

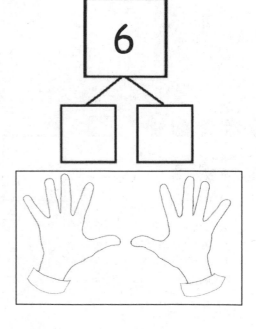

EUREKA MATH

Lesson 1:   Analyze and describe embedded numbers (to 10) using 5-groups and number bonds.

1

©2015 Great Minds. eureka-math.org
G1-M1-SE-B1-1.3.1-12.2015

Make a number bond that shows 5 as one part.

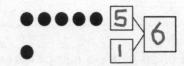

7.

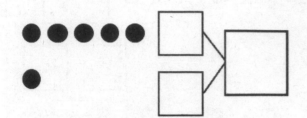

8.

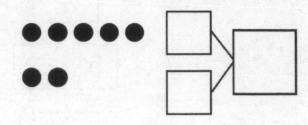

9.

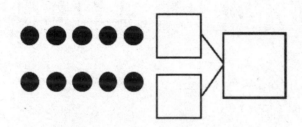

10.

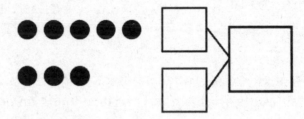

11.

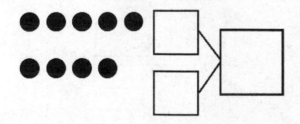

12.

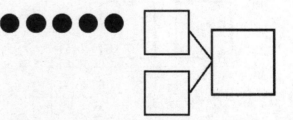

Lesson 1:   Analyze and describe embedded numbers (to 10) using 5-groups and number bonds.

EUREKA
MATH™

Name _____   Date _____

Circle 5, and then make a number bond.

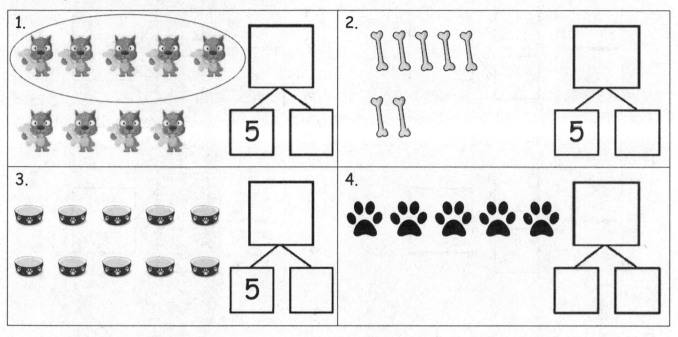

Make a number bond that shows 5 as one part.

5.

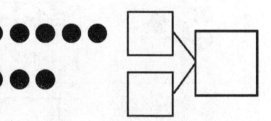

6.

7.

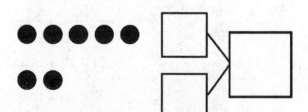

8.

EUREKA MATH™

Lesson 1:   Analyze and describe embedded numbers (to 10) using 5-groups and number bonds.

©2015 Great Minds. eureka-math.org
G1-M1-SE-B1-1.3.1-12.2015

3

Make a number bond for the dominoes.

9.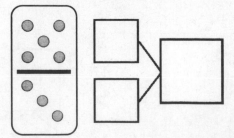

10.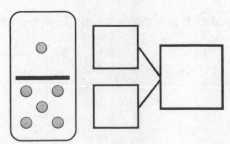

11.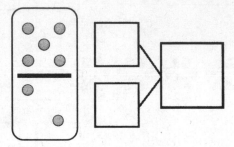

12.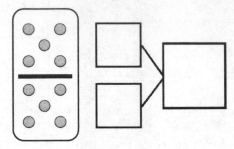

Circle 5 and count. Then, make a number bond.

13.

14.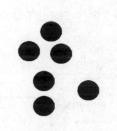

15.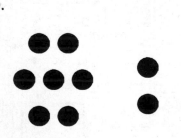

16.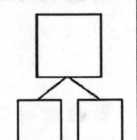

Lesson 1: Analyze and describe embedded numbers (to 10) using 5-groups and number bonds.

EUREKA MATH™

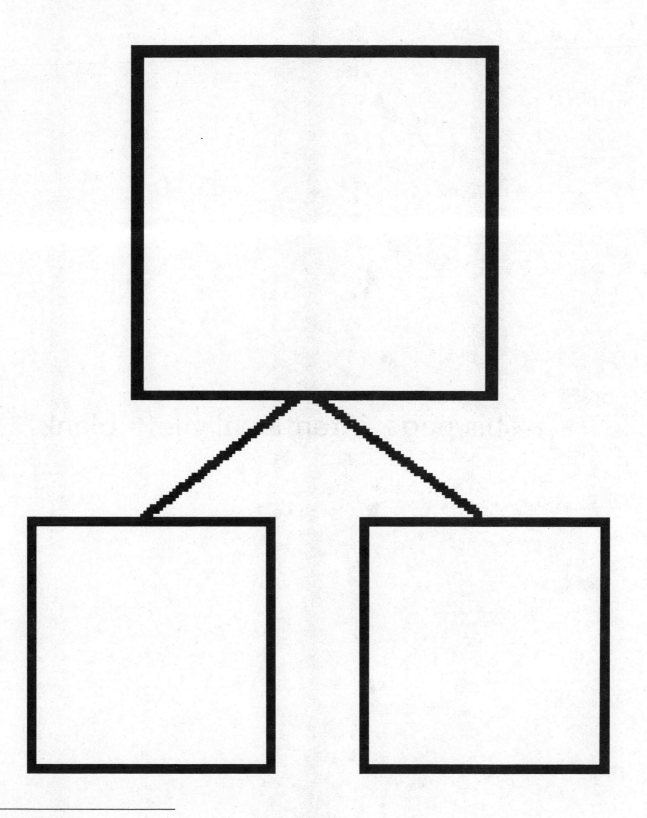

number bond

Lesson 1: Analyze and describe embedded numbers (to 10) using 5-groups and number bonds.

5

©2015 Great Minds. eureka-math.org
G1-M1-SE-B1-1.3.1-12.2015

This page intentionally left blank

Name _____   Date _____

Circle 2 parts you see. Make a number bond to match.

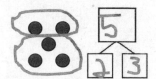

1.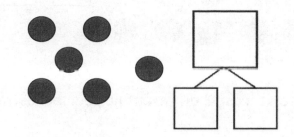

2.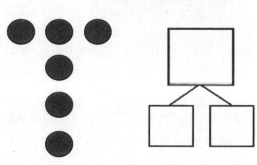

3.

4.

5.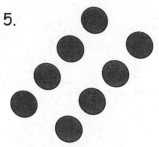

6.

Lesson 2:   Reason about embedded numbers in varied configurations using number bonds.

7

7.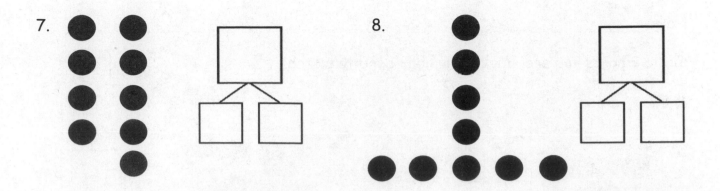

8.

9. How many pieces of fruit do you see? Write at least 2 different number bonds to show different ways to break apart the total.

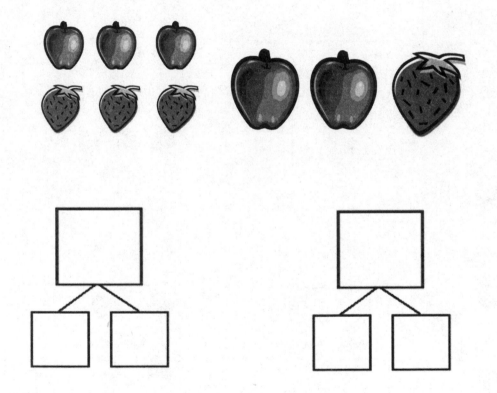

Lesson 2:   Reason about embedded numbers in varied configurations using number bonds.

EUREKA MATH

Name _____   Date _____

Circle 2 parts you see. Make a number bond to match.

1.
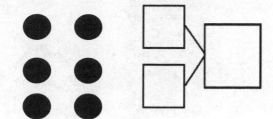

2.
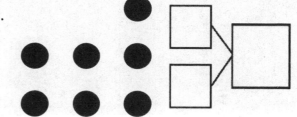

3.
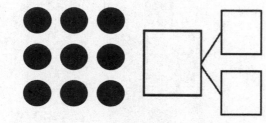

4.
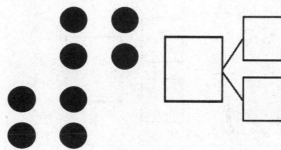

5.
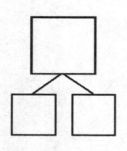

6.
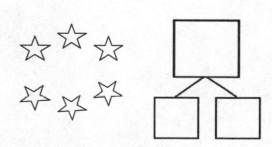

7.

8.
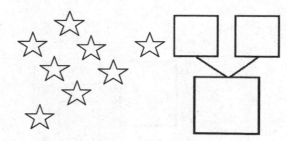

EUREKA MATH

Lesson 2:   Reason about embedded numbers in varied configurations using number bonds.

9

©2015 Great Minds. eureka-math.org
G1-M1-SE-B1-1.3.1-12.2015

How many animals do you see? Write at least 2 different number bonds to show different ways to break apart the total.

9.

10.

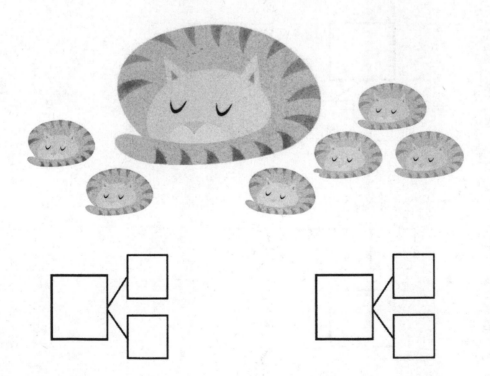

Lesson 2: Reason about embedded numbers in varied configurations using number bonds.

EUREKA MATH™

Name _____ Date _____

Draw one more in the 5-group. In the box, write the numbers to describe the new picture.

1.

2.

1 more than 7 is _____.
7 + 1 = _____

1 more than 9 is _____.
9 + 1 = _____

3.

4.

1 more than 6 is _____.
6 + 1 = _____

1 more than 5 is _____.
5 + 1 = _____

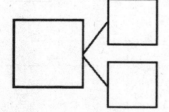

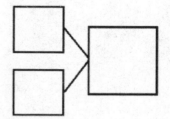

EUREKA
MATH™

Lesson 3:   See and describe numbers of objects using *1 more* within 5-group configurations.

11

©2015 Great Minds. eureka-math.org
G1-M1-SE-B1-1.3.1-12.2015

5.

1 more than 8 is _____.

8 + 1 = _____

6.

_____ is 1 more than 7.

_____ = 7 + 1

7.

_____ is 1 more than 6.

_____ = 6 + 1

8.

_____ is 1 more than 5.

_____ = 5 + 1

9. Imagine adding 1 more backpack to the picture. Then, write the numbers to match how many backpacks there will be.

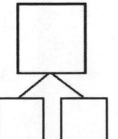

1 more than 7 is _____.

_____ + 1 = _____

Lesson 3: See and describe numbers of objects using *1 more* within 5-group configurations.

EUREKA MATH

Name _____   Date _____

How many objects do you see? Draw one more. How many objects are there now?

1.

1 more than 9 is _____.

9 + 1 = _____

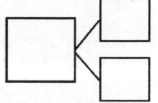

2.

_____ is 1 more than 7.

_____ = 7 + 1

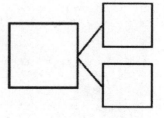

3.

_____ is 1 more than 5.

_____ = 5 + 1

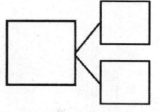

4.

1 more than 8 is _____.

_____ + 1 = _____

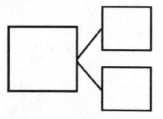

EUREKA MATH

Lesson 3:   See and describe numbers of objects using *1 more* within 5-group configurations.

13

©2015 Great Minds. eureka-math.org
G1-M1-SE-B1-1.3.1-12.2015

5. Imagine adding 1 more pencil to the picture.
    Then, write the numbers to match how many pencils there will be.

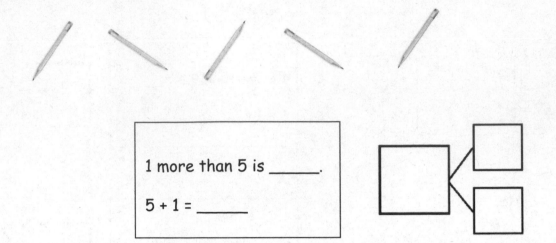

1 more than 5 is _____.

5 + 1 = _____

6. Imagine adding 1 more flower to the picture.
    Then, write the numbers to match how many flowers there will be.

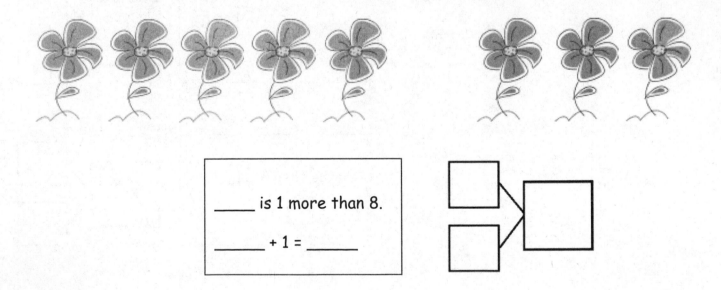

_____ is 1 more than 8.

_____ + 1 = _____

Lesson 3:   See and describe numbers of objects using *1 more* within 5-group configurations.

EUREKA
MATH™

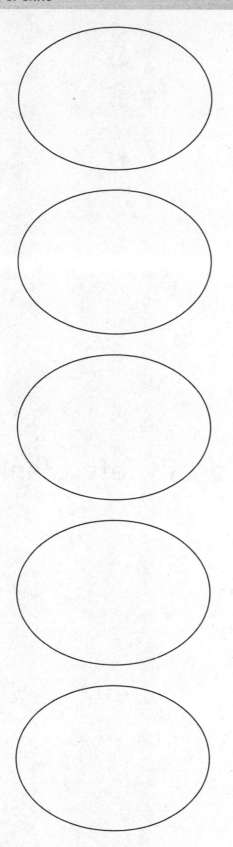
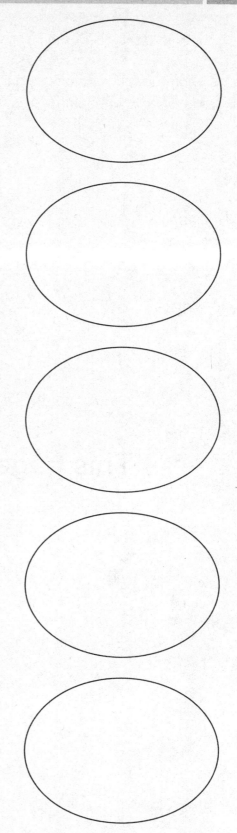

5-group mat

Lesson 3:　See and describe numbers of objects using *1 more* within 5-group configurations.

15

©2015 Great Minds. eureka-math.org
G1-M1-SE-B1-1.3.1-12.2015

This page intentionally left blank

Name _____   Date _____

Ways to Make 6.

Use the apple picture to help you write all of the different ways to make 6.

EUREKA MATH™

Lesson 4: Represent *put together* situations with number bonds. Count on from one embedded number or part to totals of 6 and 7, and generate all addition expressions for each total.

©2015 Great Minds. eureka-math.org
G1-M1-SE-B1-1.3.1-12.2015

This page intentionally left blank

Name _____   Date _____

Today, we learned the different combinations that make 6. For homework, cut out the flashcards below, and write the number sentences that you learned today on the back. Keep these flashcards in the place where you do your homework to practice ways to make 6 until you know them really well! As we continue to learn different ways to make 7, 8, 9, and 10 in the upcoming days, continue to make new flashcards.

*Note to families: Be sure students make each of the combinations that make 6. The flashcards can look something like this:

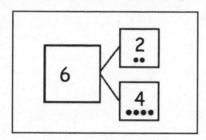

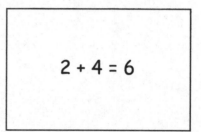

Front of Card   Back of Card

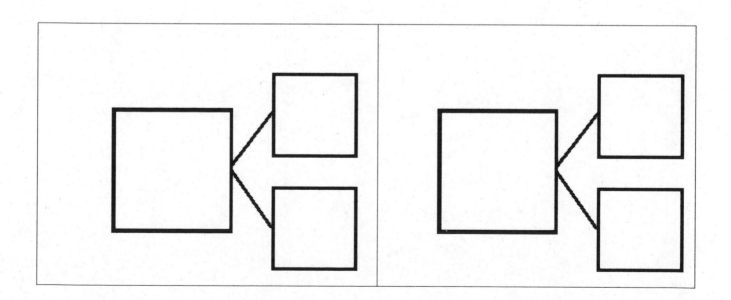

EUREKA MATH™

Lesson 4:   Represent *put together* situations with number bonds. Count on from one embedded number or part to totals of 6 and 7, and generate all addition expressions for each total.

19

©2015 Great Minds. eureka-math.org
G1-M1-SE-B1-1.3.1-12.2015

This page intentionally left blank

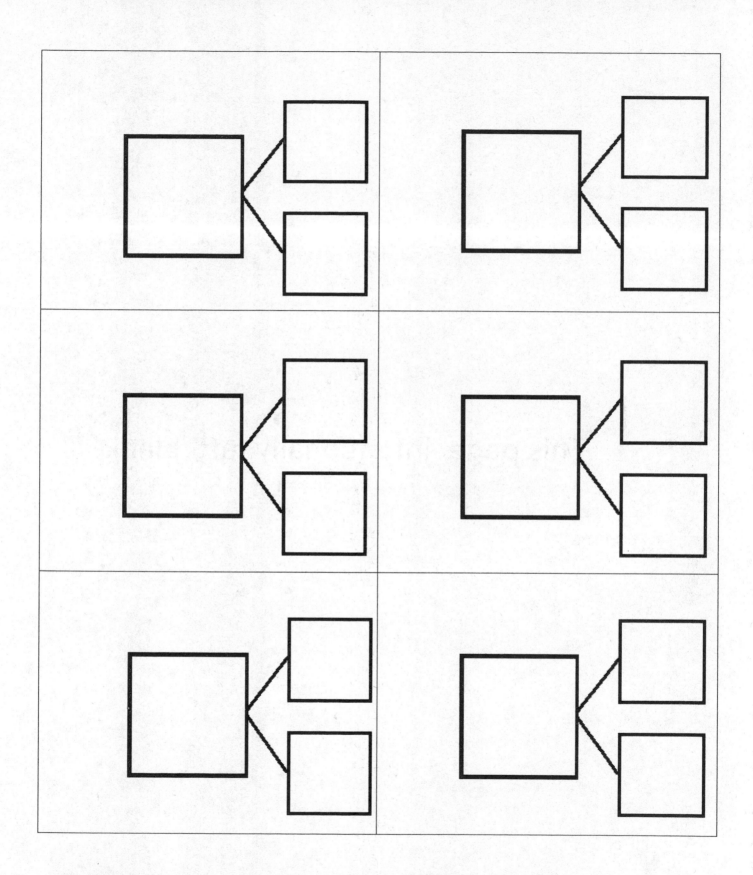

Lesson 4: Represent *put together* situations with number bonds. Count on from one embedded number or part to totals of 6 and 7, and generate all addition expressions for each total.

21

EUREKA
MATH™

This page intentionally left blank

6 apples picture card

Lesson 4:   Represent *put together* situations with number bonds. Count on from
one embedded number or part to totals of 6 and 7, and generate all
addition expressions for each total.

23

©2015 Great Minds. eureka-math.org
G1-M1-SE-B1-1.3.1-12.2015

This page intentionally left blank

Name _____   Date _____

Ways to Make 7. Use the classroom picture to help you write the expressions and number bonds to show all of the different ways to make 7.

Lesson 5:   Represent *put together* situations with number bonds. Count on from one embedded number or part to totals of 6 and 7, and generate all addition expressions for each total.

©2015 Great Minds. eureka-math.org
G1-M1-SE-B1-1.3.1-12.2015

EUREKA MATH™

This page intentionally left blank

Name _____   Date _____

1. Match the dice to show different ways to make 7. Then, draw a number bond for each pair of dice.

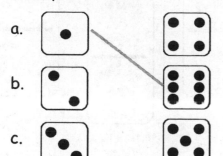 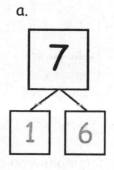 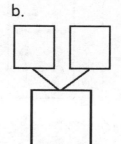 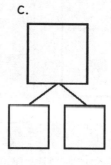

2. Make 2 number sentences. Use the number bonds above for help.

☐ (+) ☐ = 7

7 = ☐ (+) ☐

3. Fill in the missing number in the number bond. Then, write addition number sentences for the number bond you made.

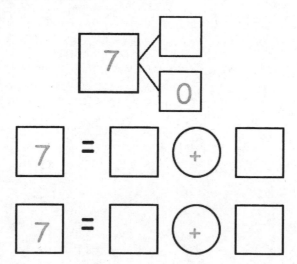

7 = ☐ (+) ☐

7 = ☐ (+) ☐

Lesson 5:   Represent *put together* situations with number bonds. Count on from one embedded number or part to totals of 6 and 7, and generate all addition expressions for each total.

27

EUREKA
MATH™

4. Color the dominoes that make 7.

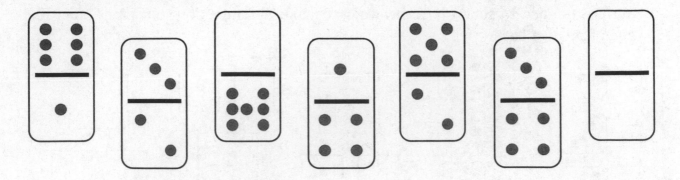

5. Complete the number bonds for the dominoes you colored.

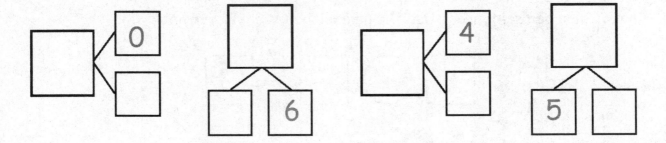

Lesson 5: Represent *put together* situations with number bonds. Count on from one embedded number or part to totals of 6 and 7, and generate all addition expressions for each total.

EUREKA MATH™

7 children picture card

EUREKA
MATH

Lesson 5:   Represent *put together* situations with number bonds. Count on from
one embedded number or part to totals of 6 and 7, and generate all
addition expressions for each total.

29

©2015 Great Minds. eureka-math.org
G1-M1-SE-B1-1.3.1-12.2015

This page intentionally left blank

Name _____   Date _____

Circle the part. Count on to show 8 with the picture and number bond. Write the expressions.

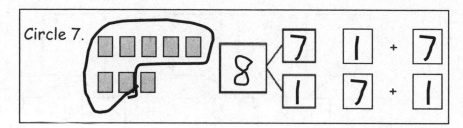

Circle 7.

1. Circle 6. How many more does 6 need to make 8?

 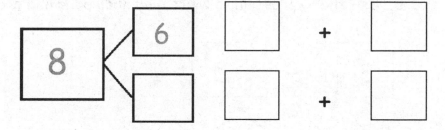

2. Circle 5. How many more does 5 need to make 8?

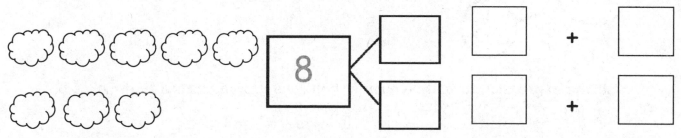

3. Circle 4. How many more does 4 need to make 8?

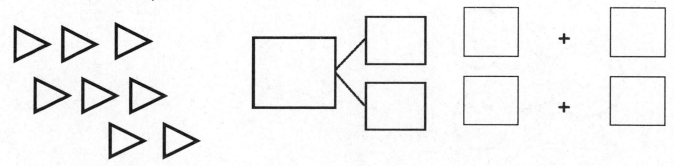

EUREKA MATH™

Lesson 6:   Represent *put together* situations with number bonds. Count on from one embedded number or part to totals of 8 and 9, and generate all expressions for each total.

31

©2015 Great Minds. eureka-math.org
G1-M1-SE-B1-1.3.1-12.2015

4. These number bonds are in an order starting with the biggest part first. Write to show which number bonds are missing.

a. 8 → 8 0   b. 8 → 7 ☐   c. 8 → 6 ☐   d. 8 → ☐ 3   e. 8 → ☐ ☐

5. Use the expression to write a number bond and draw a picture that makes 8.

☐ 3 + ☐ 5

6. Use the expression to write a number bond and draw a picture that makes 8.

☐ 8 + ☐ 0

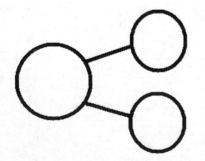

Lesson 6:   Represent *put together* situations with number bonds. Count on from one embedded number or part to totals of 8 and 9, and generate all expressions for each total.

EUREKA MATH

Name _____ Date _____

1. Match the dots to show different ways to make 8. Then, draw a number bond for each pair.

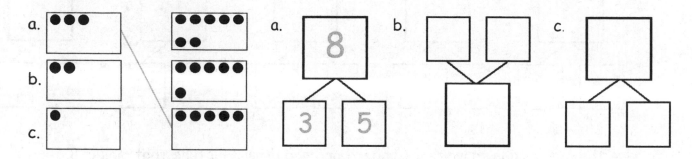

2. Show 2 ways to make 8. Use the number bonds above for help.

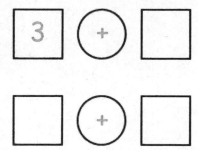

3. Fill in the missing number in the number bond. Write 2 addition sentences for the number bond you made. Notice where the equal sign is to make your sentence true.

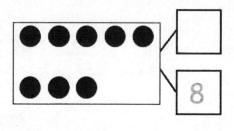

EUREKA MATH™

Lesson 6:   Represent *put together* situations with number bonds. Count on from one embedded number or part to totals of 8 and 9, and generate all expressions for each total.

33

©2015 Great Minds. eureka-math.org
G1-M1-SE-B1-1.3.1-12.2015

4. These number bonds are in an order starting with the smallest part first. Write to show which number bonds are missing.

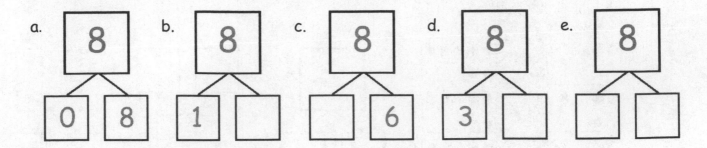

a. 8 / 0 8
b. 8 / 1 ☐
c. 8 / ☐ 6
d. 8 / 3 ☐
e. 8 / ☐ ☐

5. Use the expression to write a number bond and draw a picture that makes 8.

2 + 6

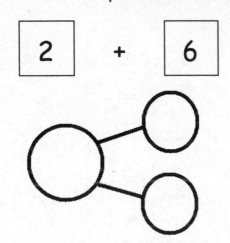

6. Use the expression to write a number bond and draw a picture that makes 8.

0 + 8

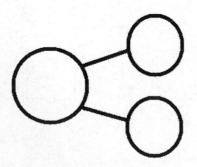

Lesson 6: Represent *put together* situations with number bonds. Count on from one embedded number or part to totals of 8 and 9, and generate all expressions for each total.

EUREKA MATH

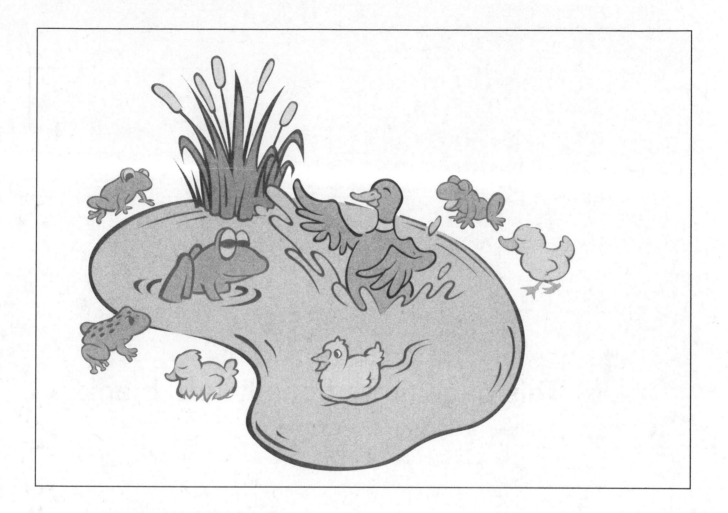

8 animals picture card

Lesson 6:   Represent *put together* situations with number bonds. Count on from one embedded number or part to totals of 8 and 9, and generate all expressions for each total.

35

This page intentionally left blank

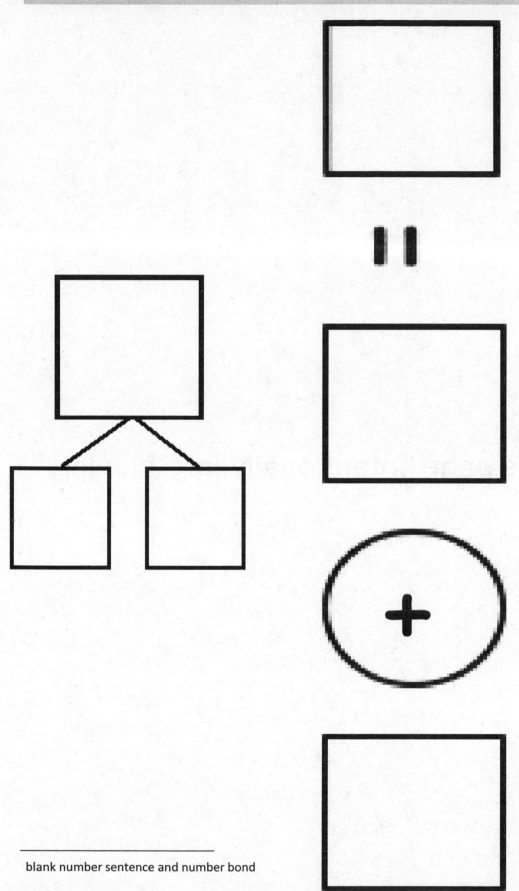

blank number sentence and number bond

Lesson 6: Represent *put together* situations with number bonds. Count on from one embedded number or part to totals of 8 and 9, and generate all expressions for each total.

37

This page intentionally left blank

Name _____　Date _____

Use your 5-group cards to help you write the expressions and number bonds to show all of the different ways to make 8.

☐ + ☐

☐ + ☐

☐ ⟨ ☐ ☐

☐ ☐ ⟩ ☐

☐ + ☐

☐ + ☐

☐ + ☐

☐ + ☐

☐ ⟨ ☐ ☐

☐ ☐ ⟩ ☐

☐ + ☐

☐ + ☐

☐ + ☐

☐ + ☐

☐ ⟨ ☐ ☐

ways to make 8

Lesson 6:　Represent *put together* situations with number bonds. Count on from one embedded number or part to totals of 8 and 9, and generate all expressions for each total.

39

©2015 Great Minds. eureka-math.org
G1-M1-SE-B1-1.3.1-12.2015

This page intentionally left blank

Name _____ Date _____

Circle the part. Count on to show 9 with the picture and number bond. Write the expressions.

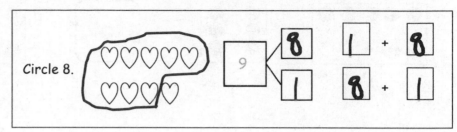

Circle 8.

1. Circle 7. How many more does 7 need to make 9?

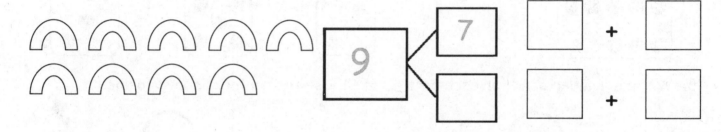

2. Circle 4. How many more does 4 need to make 9?

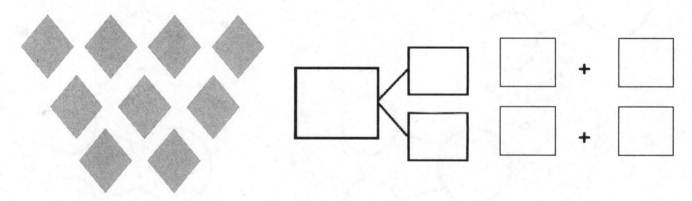

3. Circle 3. How many more does 3 need to make 9?

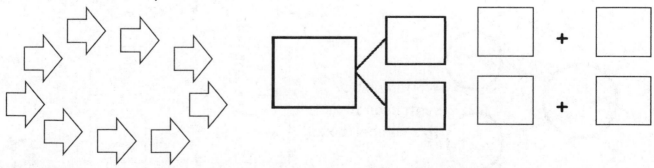

EUREKA MATH

Lesson 7: Represent *put together* situations with number bonds. Count on from one embedded number or part to totals of 8 and 9, and generate all expressions for each total.

41

©2015 Great Minds. eureka-math.org
G1-M1-SE-B1-1.3.1-12.2015

4. Draw a line to show partners of 9.

a. 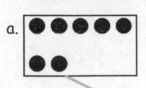 b. c. 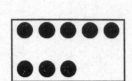 d.  e.

5. Write a number bond for each partner of 9. Use the partners above for help.

a.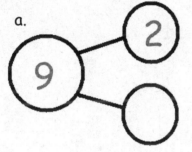

b.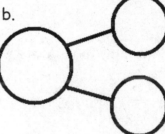

c.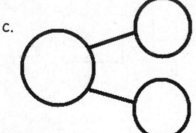

d.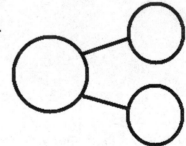

e. 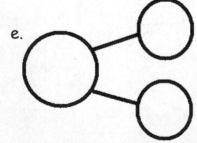 Write number sentences to match this number bond!

☐ + ☐ = ☐

☐ + ☐ = ☐

Lesson 7: Represent *put together* situations with number bonds. Count on from one embedded number or part to totals of 8 and 9, and generate all expressions for each total.

EUREKA MATH™

Name _____ Date _____

Ways to Make 9

Use the bookshelf picture to help you write the expressions and number bonds to show all of the different ways to make 9.

Lesson 7: Represent *put together* situations with number bonds. Count on from one embedded number or part to totals of 8 and 9, and generate all expressions for each total.

EUREKA MATH

©2015 Great Minds. eureka-math.org
G1-M1-SE-B1-1.3.1-12.2015

This page intentionally left blank

9 books picture card

Lesson 7:   Represent *put together* situations with number bonds. Count on from
one embedded number or part to totals of 8 and 9, and generate all
expressions for each total.

45

©2015 Great Minds. eureka-math.org
G1-M1-SE-B1-1.3.1-12.2015

This page intentionally left blank

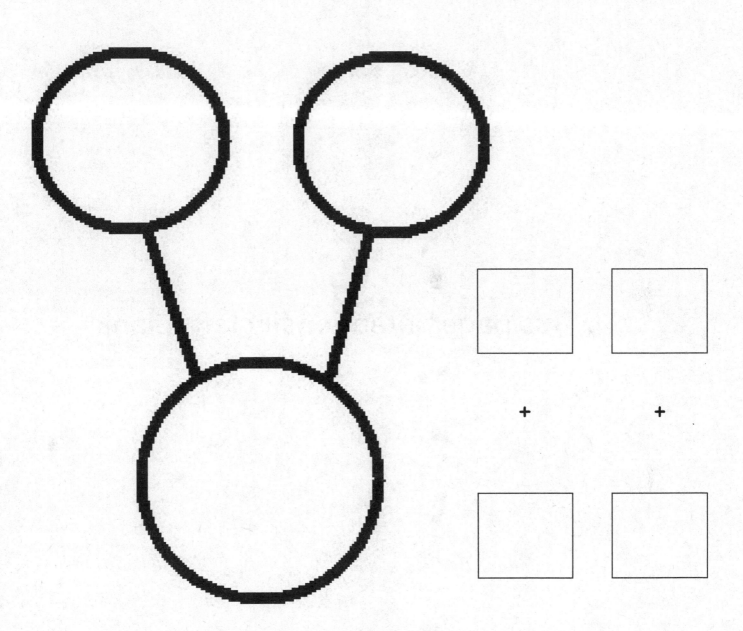

+ +

number bond and expression

Lesson 7: Represent *put together* situations with number bonds. Count on from one embedded number or part to totals of 8 and 9, and generate all expressions for each total.

This page intentionally left blank

Name _____   Date _____

1. Use your bracelet to show different partners of 10. Then, draw the beads.
   Write an expression to match.

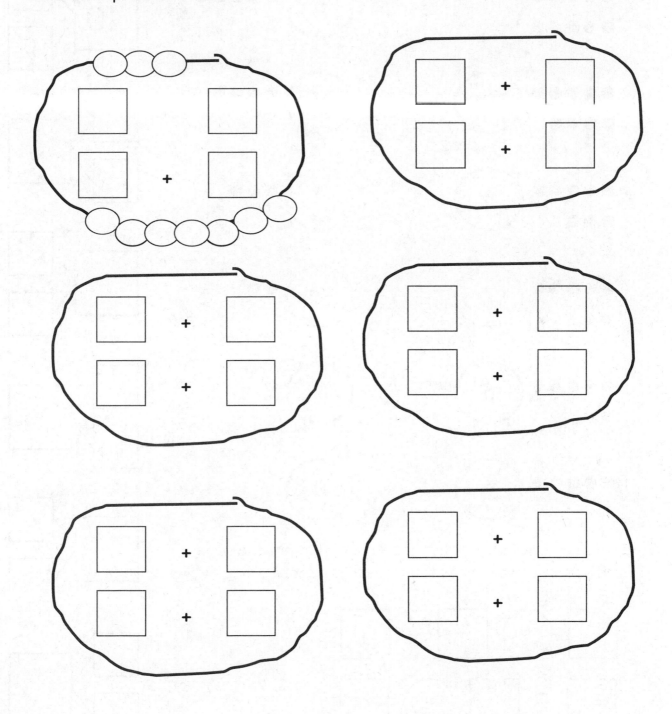

EUREKA MATH™

Lesson 8:   Represent all the number pairs of 10 as number bonds from a given
scenario, and generate all expressions equal to 10.

©2015 Great Minds. eureka-math.org
G1-M1-SE-B1-1.3.1-12.2015

2. Match the partners of 10. Then, write a number bond for each partner.

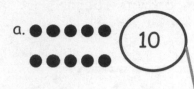 a. **10**

 **5** a.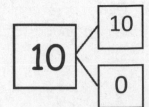

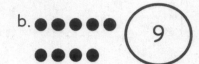 b. **9**

 **4** b.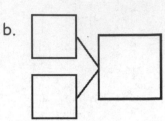

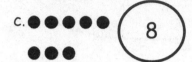 c. **8**

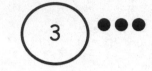 **3** c.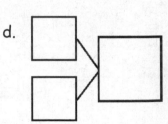

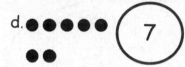 d. **7**

 **2** d.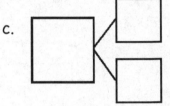

 e. **6**

1 e.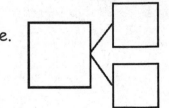

f. **5**

0 f.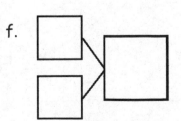

3. Color the number bond that has 2 parts that are the same. Write addition sentences to match that number bond.

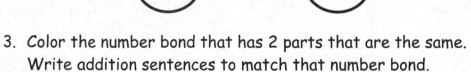

Lesson 8: Represent all the number pairs of 10 as number bonds from a given scenario, and generate all expressions equal to 10.

©2015 Great Minds. eureka-math.org
G1-M1-SE-B1-1.3.1-12.2015

EUREKA MATH™

Name _____ Date _____

1. Rex found 10 bones on his walk. He can't decide which part he wants to bring to his doghouse and which part he should bury. Help show Rex his choices by filling in the missing parts of the number bonds.

a.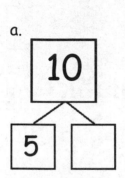

b.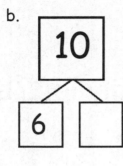

c.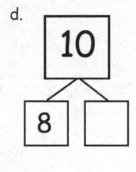

d.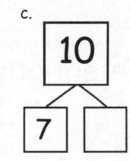

e.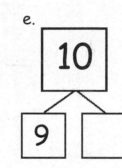

2. He decided to bury 3 and bring 7 back home. Write all the adding sentences that match this number bond.

bones

$\boxed{10}$ — $\boxed{3}$ bury

— $\boxed{7}$ home

☐ + ☐ = ☐

☐ + ☐ = ☐

☐ = ☐ + ☐

☐ = ☐ + ☐

EUREKA MATH™

Lesson 8: Represent all the number pairs of 10 as number bonds from a given scenario, and generate all expressions equal to 10.

51

This page intentionally left blank

Name _____   Date _____

1.

[ ] + [ ] = [ ]

_____ balls are here.   _____ more roll over.   Now, there are _____ balls.

Make a number bond to match the story.

___

2.

[ ] + [ ] = [ ]

_____ frogs are here.   _____ more hops over.   Now, there are _____ frogs.

Make a number bond to match the story.

EUREKA MATH

Lesson 9:   Solve *add to with result unknown* and *put together with result unknown* math stories by drawing, writing equations, and making statements of the solution.

53

©2015 Great Minds. eureka-math.org
G1-M1-SE-B1-1.3.1-12.2015

3.

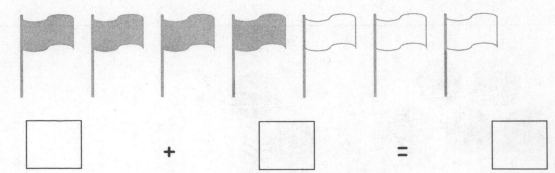

There are _____ dark flags.   There are ___ white flags.

Altogether, there are _____ flags.

Make a number bond to match the story.

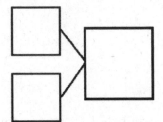

4.

There are _____ white flowers.   There are ___ dark flowers.

Altogether, there are _____ flowers.

Make a number bond to match the story.

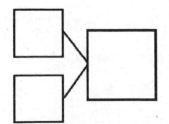

Lesson 9:   Solve *add to with result unknown* and *put together with result unknown* math stories by drawing, writing equations, and making statements of the solution.

EUREKA
MATH™

Name _____ Date _____

1. Use the picture to tell a math story.

Write a number bond to match your story.

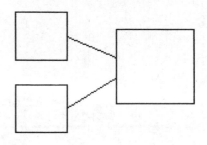

There are _____ sharks.

Write a number sentence to tell the story.

[ ] [ ] = [ ]

2. Use the picture to tell a math story.

Write a number bond to match your story.

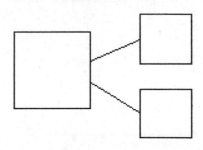

There are _____ students.

Write a number sentence to tell the story.

[ ] = [ ] + [ ]

EUREKA MATH™

Lesson 9: Solve *add to with result unknown* and *put together with result unknown* math stories by drawing, writing equations, and making statements of the solution.

©2015 Great Minds. eureka-math.org
G1-M1-SE-B1-1.3.1-12.2015

55

Draw a picture to match the story.

3. Jim has 4 big dogs and 3 small dogs. How many dogs does Jim have?

$\boxed{}$ + $\boxed{}$ = $\boxed{}$ Jim has _____ dogs.

4. Liv plays at the park. She plays with 3 girls and 6 boys. How many kids does she play with at the park?

$\boxed{}$ = $\boxed{}$ + $\boxed{}$ Liv plays with _____ kids.

Lesson 9:   Solve *add to with result unknown* and *put together with result unknown* math stories by drawing, writing equations, and making statements of the solution.

EUREKA MATH™

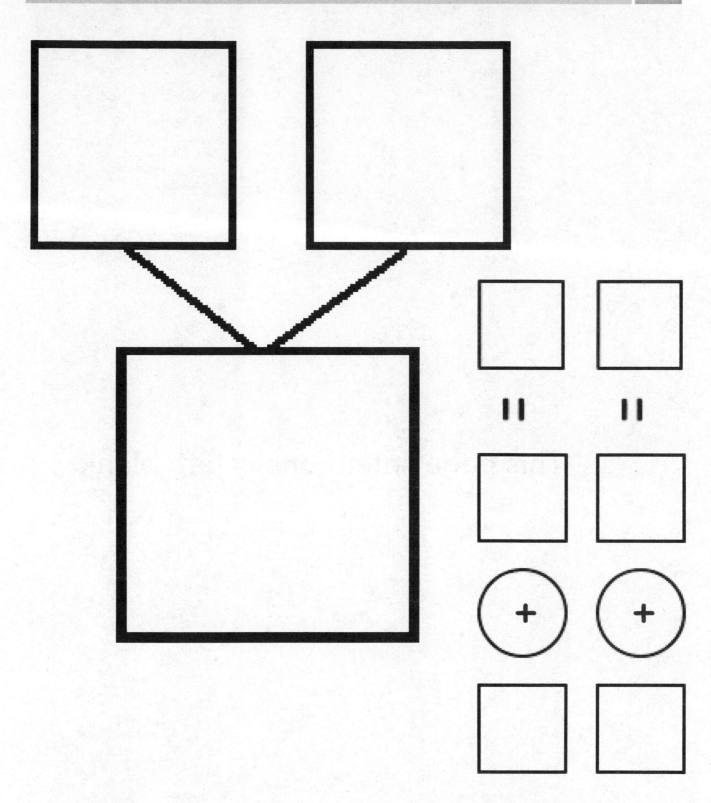

number bond and two blank equations

EUREKA MATH

Lesson 9: Solve *add to with result unknown* and *put together with result unknown* math stories by drawing, writing equations, and making statements of the solution.

57

©2015 Great Minds. eureka-math.org
G1-M1-SE-B1-1.3.1-12.2015

This page intentionally left blank

Name _____ Date _____

1. Use the picture to write the number sentence and the number bond.

_____ little turtles + _____ big turtles = _____ turtles

2.

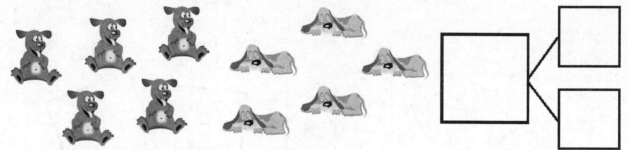

_____ dogs that are awake + _____ sleeping dogs = _____ dogs

3.

_____ pigs not in mud + _____ pigs in mud = _____ pigs

EUREKA MATH

Lesson 10: Solve *put together with result unknown* math stories by drawing and using 5-group cards.

59

4. Draw a line from the picture to the matching 5-group cards.

a.

b.

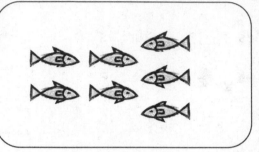   

c.

d.

Lesson 10:   Solve *put together with result unknown* math stories by drawing and using 5-group cards.

EUREKA
MATH™

Name _____   Date _____

1. Use your 5-group cards to solve.

Draw the other 5-group card to show what you did.

| | + | | = | |

5

---

2. Use your 5-group cards to solve.

Draw the other 5-group card to show what you did.

| | = | | + | |

4

EUREKA MATH

Lesson 10:   Solve *put together with result unknown* math stories by drawing and using 5-group cards.

61

©2015 Great Minds. eureka-math.org
G1-M1-SE-B1-1.3.1-12.2015

3. There are 4 tall boys and 5 short boys. Draw to show how many boys there are in all.

Write a number bond to match the story.

There are _____ boys in all.

Write a number sentence to show what you did.

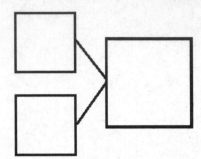

4. There are 3 girls and 5 boys. Draw to show how many children there are altogether.

Write a number bond to match the story.

There are _____ children altogether.

Write a number sentence to show what you did.

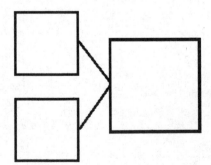

Lesson 10:   Solve *put together with result unknown* math stories by drawing and
                                          using 5-group cards.

EUREKA
MATH™

Name _____ Date _____

1. Jill was given a total of 5 flowers for her birthday. Draw more flowers in the vase to show Jill's birthday flowers.

How many flowers did you have to draw? ____ flowers

Write a number sentence and a number bond to match the story.

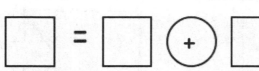 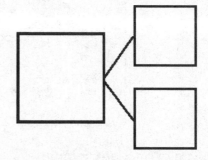

2. Kate and Nana were baking cookies. They made 2 heart cookies and then made some square cookies. They made 8 cookies altogether. How many square cookies did they make? Draw and count on to show the story.

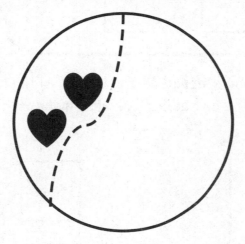

Write a number sentence and a number bond to match the story.

 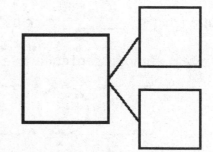

EUREKA MATH

Lesson 11: Solve *add to with change unknown* math stories as a context for counting on by drawing, writing equations, and making statements of the solution.

63

©2015 Great Minds. eureka-math.org
G1-M1-SE-B1-1.3.1-12.2015

Show the parts. Write a number bond to match the story.

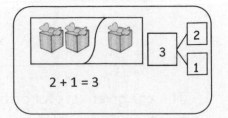

2 + 1 = 3

3. Bill has 2 trucks. His friend, James, came over with some more. Together, they had 5 trucks. How many trucks did James bring over?

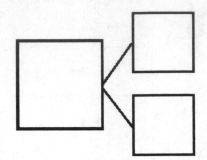

James brought over _____ trucks.

Write a number sentence to explain the story.

$$\boxed{2} \;\; \bigoplus \;\; \boxed{} \;\; = \;\; \boxed{5}$$

4. Jane caught 7 fish before she stopped to eat lunch. After lunch, she caught some more. At the end of the day, she had 9 fish. How many fish did she catch after lunch?

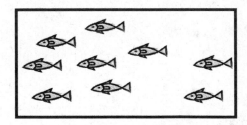

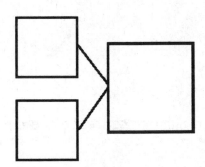

Jane caught _____ fish after lunch.

Write a number sentence to explain the story.

$$\boxed{} \;\; \bigoplus \;\; \boxed{} \;\; = \;\; \boxed{}$$

Lesson 11:   Solve *add to with change unknown* math stories as a context for counting on by drawing, writing equations, and making statements of the solution.

©2015 Great Minds. eureka-math.org
G1-M1-SE-B1-1.3.1-12.2015

EUREKA MATH™

Name _____ Date _____

1. Use the 5-group cards to count on to find the missing number in the number sentences.

a. 2 + ⬚ = 7

b. 8 = 5 + ⬚

c. 9 = 7 + ⬚

d. 9 = ⬚ + 9

EUREKA MATH™   Lesson 11:   Solve *add to with change unknown* math stories as a context for   65
counting on by drawing, writing equations, and making statements of
the solution.

©2015 Great Minds. eureka-math.org
G1-M1-SE-B1-1.3.1-12.2015

2. Match the number sentence to the math story. Draw a picture or use your 5-group cards to solve.

a. Scott has 3 cookies. His mom gives him some more. Now, he has 8 cookies. How many cookies did his mom give him?

Scott's mom gave him _____ cookies.

$$6 + \boxed{?} = 9$$

$$3 + \boxed{?} = 8$$

b. Kim sees 6 birds in the tree.

Some more birds fly in.

Kim sees 9 birds in the tree. How many birds flew to the tree?

_____ birds flew to the tree.

$$4 + \boxed{?} = 8$$

Lesson 11:   Solve *add to with change unknown* math stories as a context for counting on by drawing, writing equations, and making statements of the solution.

©2015 Great Minds. eureka-math.org
G1-M1-SE-B1-1.3.1-12.2015

EUREKA MATH

Name _____   Date _____

Use your

4 •••••

5-group cards

Fill in the missing numbers.

1.

?

3   +   _____   =   5

2.

?

5   +   _____   =   9

3.

?

4   +   _____   =   10

EUREKA MATH™

Lesson 12:   Solve *add to with change unknown* math stories using 5-group cards.

67

4. Kate and Bob had 6 balls at the park. Kate had 2 of the balls.

How many balls did Bob have?

_____ balls **=** _____ balls **+** _____ balls

Bob had _____ balls at the park.

---

5. I had 3 apples. My mom gave me some more. Then, I had 10 apples.

How many apples did my mom give me?

_____ apples **+** _____ apples **=** _____ apples

Mom gave me _____ apples.

EUREKA
MATH™

Name _____   Date _____

 Use your 5-group cards to count on to find the missing number in the number sentences.

1. [5] + [?] = [7]

   The mystery number is [ ]

    [5] [ ]

2. [2] + [?] = [8]

   The mystery number is [ ]

   [2] [ ]

3. [6] + [?] = [9]

   The mystery number is [ ]

   [6] [ ]

Use your 5-group cards to count on and solve the math stories. Use the boxes to show your 5-group cards.

4. Jack reads 4 books on Monday. He reads some more on Tuesday. He reads 7 books total. How many books does Jack read on Tuesday?

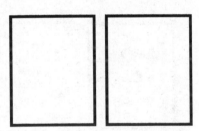

Jack reads _____ books on Tuesday.

5. Kate has 1 sister and some brothers. She has 7 brothers and sisters in all. How many brothers does Kate have?

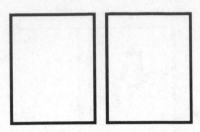

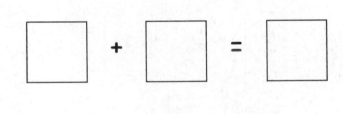

Kate has _____ brothers.

6. There are 6 dogs in the park and some cats. There are 9 dogs and cats in the park altogether. How many cats are in the park?

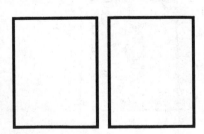

There are _____ cats total.

Solve *add to with change unknown* math stories using 5-group cards.

EUREKA MATH™

Name _____ Date _____

With a partner, create a story for each of the number sentences below. Draw a picture to show. Write the number bond to match the story.

1.   6 + 2 = ☐

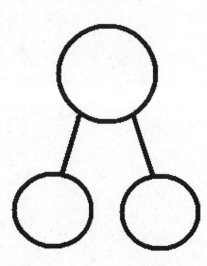

---

2.   5 + 5 = ☐

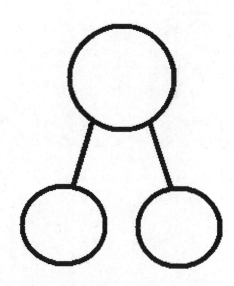

EUREKA MATH

Lesson 13:   Tell *put together with result unknown, add to with result unknown add to with change unknown* stories from equations.

71

©2015 Great Minds. eureka-math.org
G1-M1-SE-B1-1.3.1-12.2015

3.   5 + ☐ = 7

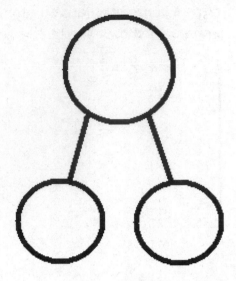

---

4.   6 + ☐ = 10

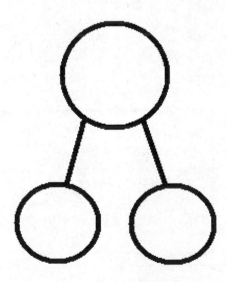

Lesson 13: Tell *put together with result unknown, add to with result unknown add to with change unknown* stories from equations.

EUREKA
MATH™

©2015 Great Minds. eureka-math.org
G1-M1-SE-B1-1.3.1-12.2015

Name _____ Date _____

Use the number sentences to draw a picture, and fill in the number bond to tell a math story.

1. 5 + 2 = 7

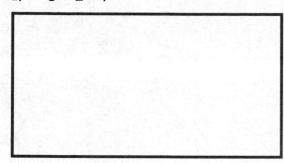   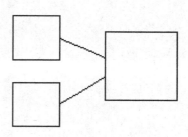

2. 3 + 6 = 9

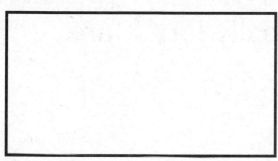   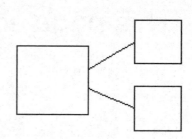

3. 7 + ? = 9

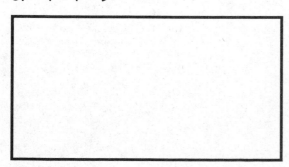   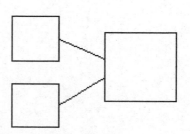

EUREKA
MATH™

Lesson 13: Tell *put together with result unknown, add to with result unknown add to with change unknown* stories from equations.

73

©2015 Great Minds. eureka-math.org
G1-M1-SE-B1-1.3.1-12.2015

This page intentionally left blank

Name _____   Date _____

1. Count on to add.

☐ ⊕ ☐ = ☐   There are _____ flowers altogether.

2.

☐ = ☐ ⊕ ☐   There are _____ oranges in all.

3.

☐ = ☐ ⊕ ☐   There is a total of _____ crayons.

EUREKA MATH

Lesson 14:   Count on up to 3 more using numeral and 5-group cards and fingers to track the change.

75

4. Use your 5-group cards to count on to add. Try to use as few dot cards as you can.

a. $6 \, + \, 1 \, = \, \boxed{}$

b. $6 \, + \, 3 \, = \, \boxed{}$

c. $7 \, + \, 2 \, = \, \boxed{}$

d. $\boxed{} \, = \, 5 \, + \, 3$

5. Use your 5-group cards, your fingers, or your known facts to count on to add.

a. $8 \, + \, 2 \, = \, \boxed{}$

b. $\boxed{} \, = \, 4 \, + \, 1$

c. $4 \, + \, 3 \, = \, \boxed{}$

d. $\boxed{} \, = \, 6 \, + \, 3$

EUREKA
MATH™

Name _____ Date _____

Count on to add.

a.

| 5 | + | 1 | = | |

Write what you say
when you count on.

b.

| 5 | + | 2 | = | |

c.

| 7 | + | 2 | = | |

d.

| | = | 6 | + | 3 |

e.

| | = | 7 | + | |

EUREKA MATH

Lesson 14: Count on up to 3 more using numeral and 5-group cards and fingers
to track the change.

77

©2015 Great Minds. eureka-math.org
G1-M1-SE-B1-1.3.1-12.2015

This page intentionally left blank

Name _____ Date _____

1. Count on to add.

a.

☐ (+) ☐ = ☐   There are ____ crayons altogether.

b.

☐ (+) ☐ = ☐   There are a total of ____ balloons.

c.

 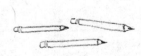

☐ = ☐ (+) ☐   In all, there are ____ pencils.

EUREKA MATH™

Lesson 15: Count on up to 3 more using numeral and 5-group cards and fingers to track the change.

79

©2015 Great Minds. eureka-math.org
G1-M1-SE-B1-1.3.1-12.2015

2. What shortcut or efficient strategy can you find to add?

a. 4 (+) 1 = ☐   h. 2 (+) 5 = ☐

b. 4 (+) 3 = ☐   i. 7 (+) 2 = ☐

c. 7 (+) 1 = ☐   j. 7 (+) 3 = ☐

d. ☐ = 6 (+) 2   k. ☐ = 4 (+) 2

e. ☐ = 5 (+) 3   l. ☐ = 2 (+) 5

f. ☐ = 3 (+) 6   m. ☐ = 6 (+) 2

g. ☐ = 3 (+) 7   n. ☐ = 2 (+) 8

Lesson 15:   Count on up to 3 more using numeral and 5-group cards and fingers
to track the change.

©2015 Great Minds. eureka-math.org
G1-M1-SE-B1-1.3.1-12.2015

EUREKA MATH

Name _____   Date _____

    Use your 5-group cards or your fingers to count on to solve.

Show the shortcut you used to add.

1. [5] (+) [3] = [ ]

2. [6] (+) [2] = [ ]

3. [7] (+) [3] = [ ]

Show the strategy you used to add.

4. [ ] = [8] (+) [2]

5. [ ] = [6] (+) [3]

6. [ ] = [7] (+) [2]

EUREKA MATH

Lesson 15:   Count on up to 3 more using numeral and 5-group cards and fingers
to track the change.

81

This page intentionally left blank

Name _____ Date _____

1. Draw more apples to solve 4 + ? = 6.

$$\boxed{4} \ \textcircled{+} \ \boxed{} \ = \ \boxed{6}$$

| I added _____ apples to the tree. |

2. How many more to make 7?

$$\boxed{5} \ \textcircled{+} \ \boxed{} \ = \ \boxed{7}$$

3. How many more to make 8?

$$\boxed{6} \ \textcircled{+} \ \boxed{} \ = \ \boxed{8}$$

4. How many more to make 9?

$$\boxed{7} \ \textcircled{+} \ \boxed{} \ = \ \boxed{9}$$

EUREKA MATH™

Lesson 16:   Count on to find the unknown part in missing addend equations such as 6 + __ = 9. Answer, "How many more to make 6, 7, 8, 9, and 10?"

83

©2015 Great Minds. eureka-math.org
G1-M1-SE-B1-1.3.1-12.2015

$$3 \; \bigoplus \; 1 \; = \; 4$$

5. Count on to add. (Circle) the strategy you used to keep track.

a. $4 \; \bigoplus \; \boxed{} \; = \; 5$

b. $4 \; \bigoplus \; \boxed{} \; = \; 7$

c. $8 \; = \; 5 \; \bigoplus \; \boxed{}$

d. $10 \; = \; \boxed{} \; \bigoplus \; 8$

e. $7 \; \bigoplus \; \boxed{} \; = \; 8$

f. $\boxed{} \; \bigoplus \; 5 \; = \; 7$

g. $8 \; = \; 6 \; \bigoplus \; \boxed{}$

h. $10 \; = \; \boxed{} \; \bigoplus \; 7$

Lesson 16: Count on to find the unknown part in missing addend equations such as 6 + __ = 9. Answer, "How many more to make 6, 7, 8, 9, and 10?"

EUREKA MATH™

Name _____   Date _____

1. Use simple math drawings. Draw more to solve 4 + ? = 6.

= | 6 |

4   +   [   ]   = | 6 |

2. Use your 5-group cards to solve 6 + ? = 8

6

= | 8 |

6   +   [   ]   = | 8 |

3. Use counting on to solve 7 + ? = 10

7...

7   +   [   ]   = | 10 |

EUREKA MATH

Lesson 16:   Count on to find the unknown part in missing addend equations such
as 6 + __ = 9. Answer, "How many more to make 6, 7, 8, 9, and 10?"

85

©2015 Great Minds. eureka-math.org
G1-M1-SE-B1-1.3.1-12.2015

This page intentionally left blank

Name _____   Date _____

Write an expression that matches the groups on each plate. If the plates have the same amount of fruit, write the equal sign between the expressions.

$$\boxed{} + \boxed{} \quad \bigcirc\!\!\!= \quad \boxed{} + \boxed{}$$

2   3   1   4

1.

$$\boxed{} + \boxed{} \quad \bigcirc \quad \boxed{} + \boxed{}$$

2.

$$\boxed{} + \boxed{} \quad \bigcirc \quad \boxed{} + \boxed{}$$

3.

$$\boxed{} + \boxed{} \quad \bigcirc \quad \boxed{} + \boxed{}$$

4.

$$\boxed{} + \boxed{} \quad \bigcirc \quad \boxed{} + \boxed{}$$

EUREKA MATH™

Lesson 17:   Understand the meaning of the equal sign by pairing equivalent expressions and constructing true number sentences.

87

©2015 Great Minds. eureka-math.org
G1-M1-SE-B1-1.3.1-12.2015

5. Write an expression to match each domino.

2+5

a.

b.

c.

_____

_____

_____

d.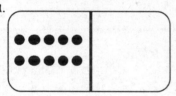

e.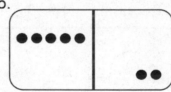

f.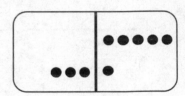

_____

_____

_____

g. Find two sets of expressions from (a)–(f) that are equal. Connect them below with = to make true number sentences.

_____   _____

6. a.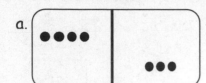

b.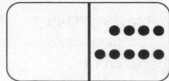

c.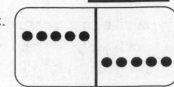

_____

_____

_____

d.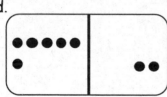

e.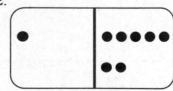

f.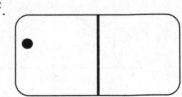

_____

_____

_____

g. Find two sets of expressions from (a)–(f) that are equal. Connect them below with = to make true number sentences.

_____   _____

Lesson 17:   Understand the meaning of the equal sign by pairing equivalent
expressions and constructing true number sentences.

EUREKA
MATH™

Name _____   Date _____

1. Match the equal dominoes. Then, write true number sentences. 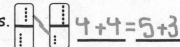 $4 + 4 = 5 + 3$

a. 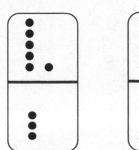   _____ _____

b. 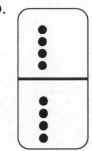   _____ _____

c. 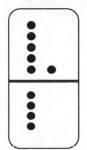   _____ _____

2. Find the expressions that are equal. Use the equal expressions to write true number sentences.

5 + 2   8 + 2   4 + 3   7 + 3

a. _____   _____

b. _____   _____

EUREKA MATH™

Lesson 17:   Understand the meaning of the equal sign by pairing equivalent expressions and constructing true number sentences.

©2015 Great Minds. eureka-math.org
G1-M1-SE-B1-1.3.1-12.2015

89

This page intentionally left blank

Name _____   Date _____

1. Add. Color the balloons that match the number in the boy's mind. Find expressions that are equal. Connect them below with = to make true number sentences.

a.

3 + 6

8 + 2

5 + 1

3 + 3

4 + 3

6

_____

b.

4 + 5

4 + 4

5 + 3

6 + 3

3 + 7

8

_____

EUREKA
MATH

Lesson 18:   Understand the meaning of the equal sign by pairing equivalent expressions and constructing true number sentences.

91

2. Are these number sentences true? if it is true. if it is false.

If it is false, rewrite the number sentence to make it true.

a. 3 + 1 = 2 + 2 ☐

b. 9 + 1 = 1 + 2

_____

_____

c. 2 + 3 = 1 + 4 ☐

d. 5 + 1 = 4 + 2

_____

_____

e. 4 + 3 = 3 + 5 ☐

f. 0 + 10 = 2 + 8

_____

_____

g. 6 + 3 = 4 + 5 ☐

h. 3 + 7 = 2 + 6

_____

_____

3. Write a number in the expression and solve. if it is true. if it is false.

a. 1 + ___ = 3 + 2 ☐

b. ___ + 4 = 2 + 5

c. ___ + 5 = 6 + ___

d. 7 + ___ = 8 + ___ ☐

Lesson 18:   Understand the meaning of the equal sign by pairing equivalent expressions and constructing true number sentences.

EUREKA MATH™

Name _____   Date _____

1. The pictures below are not equal. Make the pictures equal, and write a true number sentence.

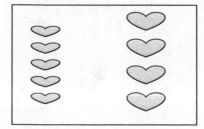   

_____   _____

2. Circle the true number sentences, and rewrite the false sentences to make them true.

a. 4 = 4

b. 5 + 1 = 6 + 1

c. 3 + 2 = 5 + 0

_____   _____   _____

d. 6 + 2 = 4 + 4

e. 3 + 3 = 6 + 2

f. 9 + 0 = 7 + 2

_____   _____   _____

g. 4 + 3 = 2 + 4

h. 8 = 8 + 0

i. 6 + 3 = 5 + 4

_____   _____   _____

EUREKA MATH

Lesson 18:   Understand the meaning of the equal sign by pairing equivalent expressions and constructing true number sentences.

93

©2015 Great Minds. eureka-math.org
G1-M1-SE-B1-1.3.1-12.2015

3. Find the missing part to make the number sentences true.

a.

$8 + 0 = \underline{\quad} + 4$

b.

$7 + 2 = 9 + \underline{\quad}$

c.

$5 + 2 = 4 + \underline{\quad}$

d.

$5 + \underline{\quad} = 6 + 0$

e.

$6 + \underline{\quad} = 4 + 3$

f.

$5 + 4 = \underline{\quad} + 3$

Lesson 18: Understand the meaning of the equal sign by pairing equivalent expressions and constructing true number sentences.

©2015 Great Minds. eureka-math.org
G1-M1-SE-B1-1.3.1-12.2015

EUREKA
MATH

Name _____ Date _____

1. Write the number bond to match the picture. Then, complete the number sentences.

a.

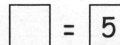  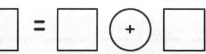 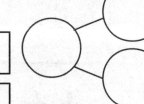

b.

  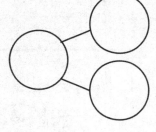

c.

 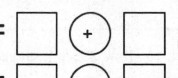 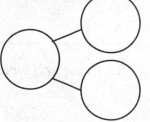

Lesson 19: Represent the same story scenario with addends repositioned (the commutative property).

95

EUREKA MATH™

©2015 Great Minds. eureka-math.org
G1-M1-SE-B1-1.3.1-12.2015

Write the expression under each plate. Add the equal sign to show they are the same amount.

2.

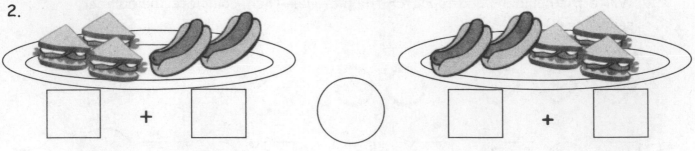

3.

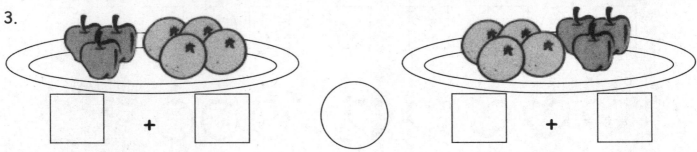

4. Draw to show the expression.

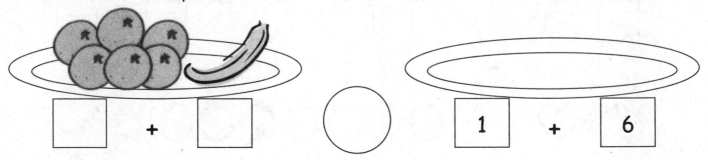

5. Draw and write to show 2 expressions that use the same numbers and have the same total.

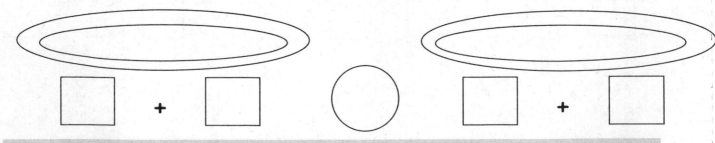

Lesson 19:   Represent the same story scenario with addends repositioned (the commutative property).

EUREKA MATH

Name _____   Date _____

1. Use the picture to write a number bond. Then, write the matching number sentences.

   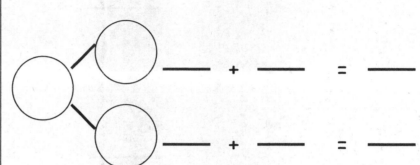

_____ + _____ = _____

_____ + _____ = _____

2. Write the number sentences to match the number bonds.

a.
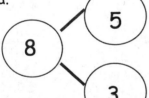

_____ + _____ = _____

_____ + _____ = _____

b.
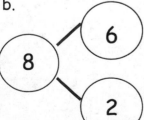

_____ = _____ + _____

_____ = _____ + _____

EUREKA MATH   **Lesson 19:**   Represent the same story scenario with addends repositioned (the   **97**
                                        commutative property).

©2015 Great Minds. eureka-math.org
G1-M1-SE-B1-1.3.1-12.2015

c.

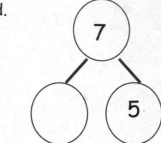

_____ + _____ = _____

_____ + _____ = _____

d.

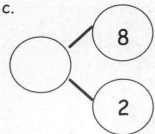

_____ + _____ = _____

_____ + _____ = _____

e.

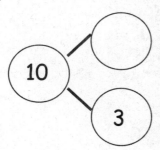

_____ = _____ + _____

_____ = _____ + _____

f.

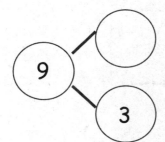

_____ + _____ = _____

_____ + _____ = _____

Lesson 19:   Represent the same story scenario with addends repositioned (the commutative property).

EUREKA MATH™

Name _____   Date _____

Circle the larger amount and count on. Write the number sentence, starting with the larger number.

1.

$\boxed{5} \; \bigcirc{+} \; \boxed{1} = \boxed{6}$

$\boxed{} \; \bigcirc{+} \; \boxed{} = \boxed{}$

Color the larger part, and complete the number bond.
Write the number sentence, starting with the larger part.

 $\boxed{3} \; \bigcirc{+} \; \boxed{1} = \boxed{4}$

2.

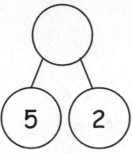

5   2

$\boxed{} \; \bigcirc{+} \; \boxed{} = \boxed{}$

3.

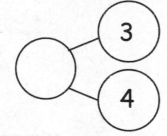

3
4

$\boxed{} \; \bigcirc{+} \; \boxed{} = \boxed{}$

4.

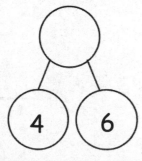

4   6

$\boxed{} \; \bigcirc{+} \; \boxed{} = \boxed{}$

EUREKA MATH™

Lesson 20:   Apply the commutative property to count on from a larger addend.

99

Color the larger part of the bond. Count on from that part to find the total, and fill in the number bond. Complete the first number sentence, and then rewrite the number sentence to start with the larger part.

5.

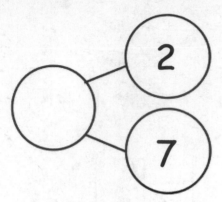

| 2 | + | ☐ | = | ☐ |

| ☐ | + | ☐ | = | ☐ |

6.

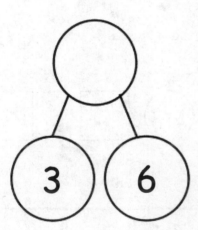

| 3 | + | ☐ | = | ☐ |

| ☐ | + | ☐ | = | ☐ |

Circle the larger number, and count on to solve.

7. 1 + 5 = _____

8. 2 + 6 = _____

9. 4 + 3 = _____

10. 3 + 6 = _____

100   Lesson 20:   Apply the commutative property to count on from a larger addend.

EUREKA MATH

Name _____ Date _____

Color the larger part, and complete the number bond.
Write the number sentence, starting with the larger part.

1.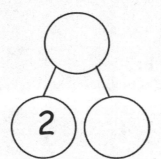

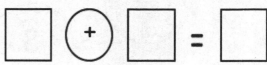

2.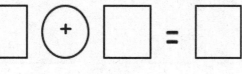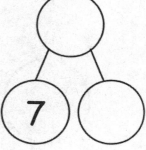

3.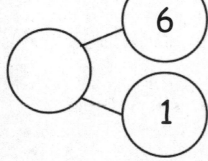

_____ + _____ = _____

4.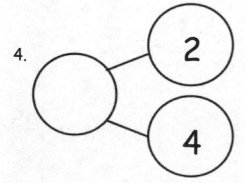

_____ + _____ = _____

Lesson 20: Apply the commutative property to count on from a larger addend.

101

5.

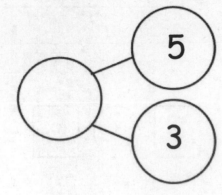

_____ + _____ = _____

6.

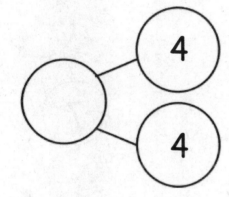

_____ + _____ = _____

7.

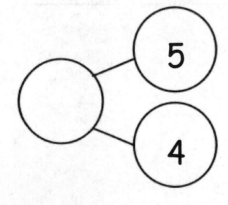

_____ + _____ = _____

Lesson 20:   Apply the commutative property to count on from a larger addend.

EUREKA MATH

Name _____   Date _____

Add the numbers on the pairs of cards. Write the number sentences. Color doubles red. Color doubles plus 1 blue.

1.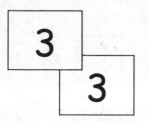

_____

2.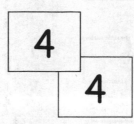

_____

3.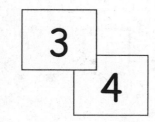

_____

4.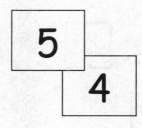

_____

Solve. Use your doubles to help. Draw and write the double that helped.

5. $5 + 4 =$

○○○○○
○○○○○

_____

6. $4 + 3 =$ ☐

○○○○○
○○○○○

_____

EUREKA MATH

Lesson 21:   Visualize and solve doubles and doubles plus 1 with 5-group cards.

103

7. Solve the doubles and the doubles plus 1 number sentences.

a. $0 + 0 = \square$ $0 + 1 = \square$

b. $2 + 2 = \square$ $2 + 3 = \square$

c. $3 + 3 = \square$ $3 + 4 = \square$

d. $4 + 4 = \square$ $4 + 5 = \square$

e. $3 + \square = 6$ $3 + \square = 7$

f. $5 + \square = 10$ $4 + \square = 9$

8. Show how this strategy can help you solve $5 + 6 = \square$

9. Write a set of 4 related addition facts for the number sentences of Problem 7(d).

Visualize and solve doubles and doubles plus 1 with 5-group cards.

EUREKA
MATH™

2

2

2+2=4

Name _____   Date _____

1. Draw the 5-group card to show a double. Write the number sentence to match the cards.

   a.
   [4]
   [ ]

   b.
   [ ]
   [3]

   c.
   [5]
   [ ]

   _____   _____   _____

2. Fill in the 5-group cards in order from least to greatest, double the number, and write the number sentences.

   a.

   b.

   c.

   _____   _____   _____

   d.
   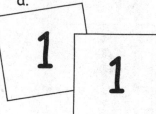

   e.
   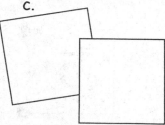

   _____   _____

EUREKA MATH

Lesson 21:   Visualize and solve doubles and doubles plus 1 with 5-group cards.

105

3. Solve the number sentences.

a. 3 + 3 = _____

b. 5 + _____ = 10

c. 1 + _____ = 2

d. 4 = _____ + 2

e. 8 = 4 + _____

4. Match the top cards to the bottom cards to show doubles plus 1.

a. 1   b. 4   c. 3   d. 2

5   2   3   4

5. Solve the number sentences. Write the double fact that helped you solve the double plus 1.

a. 2 + 3 = _____

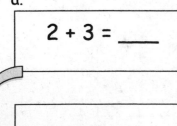

b. 3 + _____ = 7

c. 4 + _____ = 9

Lesson 21:   Visualize and solve doubles and doubles plus 1 with 5-group cards.

EUREKA MATH

1+9									
1+8	2+8								
1+7	2+7	3+7							
1+6	2+6	3+6	4+6						
1+5	2+5	3+5	4+5	5+5					
1+4	2+4	3+4	4+4	5+4	6+4				
1+3	2+3	3+3	4+3	5+3	6+3	7+3			
1+2	2+2	3+2	4+2	5+2	6+2	7+2	8+2		
1+1	2+1	3+1	4+1	5+1	6+1	7+1	8+1	9+1	
1+0	2+0	3+0	4+0	5+0	6+0	7+0	8+0	9+0	10+0

addition chart

Lesson 21:   Visualize and solve doubles and doubles plus 1 with 5-group cards.

©2015 Great Minds. eureka-math.org
G1-M1-SE-B1-1.3.1-12.2015

This page intentionally left blank

Name _____   Date _____

1. Use RED to color boxes with 0 as an addend. Find the total for each.
2. Use ORANGE to color boxes with 1 as an addend. Find the total for each.
3. Use YELLOW to color boxes with 2 as an addend. Find the total for each.
4. Use GREEN to color boxes with 3 as an addend. Find the total for each.
5. Use BLUE to color the boxes that are left. Find the total for each.

orange

| 6 + 1 |
| 7 |

1 + 0	1 + 1	1 + 2	1 + 3	1 + 4	1 + 5	1 + 6	1 + 7	1 + 8	1 + 9
2 + 0	2 + 1	2 + 2	2 + 3	2 + 4	2 + 5	2 + 6	2 + 7	2 + 8	
3 + 0	3 + 1	3 + 2	3 + 3	3 + 4	3 + 5	3 + 6	3 + 7		
4 + 0	4 + 1	4 + 2	4 + 3	4 + 4	4 + 5	4 + 6			
5 + 0	5 + 1	5 + 2	5 + 3	5 + 4	5 + 5				
6 + 0	6 + 1	6 + 2	6 + 3	6 + 4					
7 + 0	7 + 1	7 + 2	7 + 3						
8 + 0	8 + 1	8 + 2							
9 + 0	9 + 1								
10 + 0									

Name _____   Date _____

 Solve the problems without counting all. Color the boxes using the key.

Step 1: Color the problems with "+ 1" or "1 +" blue.

Step 2: Color the remaining problems with "+ 2" or "2 +" green.

Step 3: Color the remaining problems with "+ 3" or "3 +" yellow.

a. $7 + 1 = \_\_\_$	b. $8 + \_\_\_ = 9$	c. $3 + 1 = \_\_\_$	d. $5 + 3 = \_\_\_$
e. $5 + \_\_\_ = 7$	f. $4 + \_\_\_ = 7$	g. $6 + 3 = \_\_\_$	h. $8 + \_\_\_ = 10$
i. $2 + 1 = \_\_\_$	j. $1 + \_\_\_ = 2$	k. $1 + \_\_\_ = 4$	l. $6 + 2 = \_\_\_$
m. $3 + \_\_\_ = 6$	n. $6 + \_\_\_ = 7$	o. $3 + 2 = \_\_\_$	p. $5 + 1 = \_\_\_$
q. $2 + 2 = \_\_\_$	r. $4 + \_\_\_ = 6$	s. $4 + 1 = \_\_\_$	t. $7 + 2 = \_\_\_$
u. $2 + \_\_\_ = 3$	v. $9 + 1 = \_\_\_$	w. $7 + 3 = \_\_\_$	x. $1 + \_\_\_ = 3$

Lesson 22:   Look for and make use of repeated reasoning on the addition chart by solving and analyzing problems with common addends.

EUREKA MATH™

Name _____ Date _____

Use your chart to write a list of number sentences in the spaces below.

Totals of 10	Totals of 9	Totals of 8	Totals of 7

EUREKA MATH™

Lesson 23: Look for and make use of structure on the addition chart by looking for and coloring problems with the same total.

111

©2015 Great Minds. eureka-math.org
G1-M1-SE-B1-1.3.1-12.2015

Name _____   Date _____

Fill in the missing box, and find the totals for all of the expressions. Use your completed addition chart to help you.

1.

1 + 2	1 + 3
2 + 2	
3 + 2	3 + 3

2.

6 + 1	6 + 2
7 + 1	
	8 + 2
9 + 1	

3.

4 + 4	4 + 5	
5 + 4		
6 + 4		

4.

2 + 4		2 + 6
	3 + 5	

Lesson 23:   Look for and make use of structure on the addition chart by looking for and coloring problems with the same total.

©2015 Great Minds. eureka-math.org
G1-M1-SE-B1-1.3.1-12.2015

EUREKA MATH™

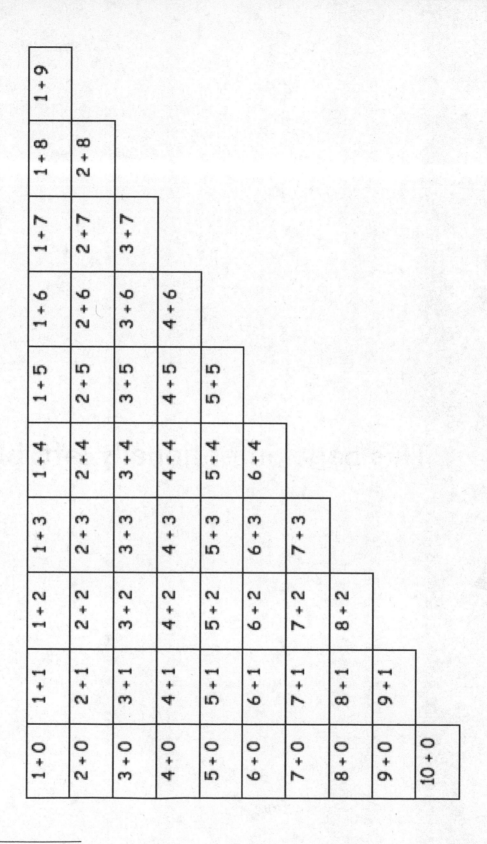

addition chart - from Lesson 21

Lesson 23: Look for and make use of structure on the addition chart by looking for and coloring problems with the same total.

113

This page intentionally left blank

Name _____ Date _____

Related Fact Ladders

1.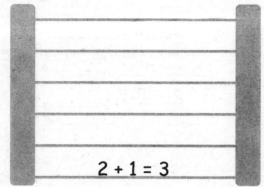
   $2 + 1 = 3$

2.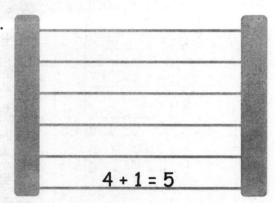
   $4 + 1 = 5$

3.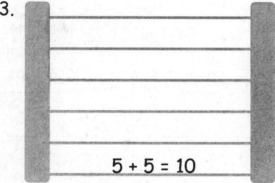
   $5 + 5 = 10$

4.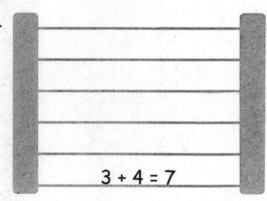
   $3 + 4 = 7$

5.
   $2 + 6 = 8$

6.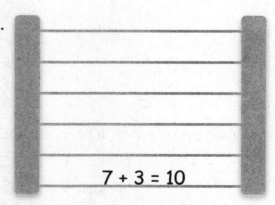
   $7 + 3 = 10$

Name _____ Date _____

Solve and sort the number sentences. One number sentence can go in more than one place when you sort.

| 5 + 1 = ___ | 6 + 2 = ___ | 2 + 3 = ___ |

| 3 + 3 = ___ | 7 + 1 = ___ | 2 + 2 = ___ |

| ___ = 4 + 4 | 8 + 2 = ___ | 3 + 4 = ___ |

| ___ = 5 + 4 | 10 = 1 + ___ | ___ = 5 + 2 |

Doubles	Doubles +1	+1	+2	Mentally visualized 5-groups

Write your own number sentences, and add them to the chart.

| | | |

Lesson 24:   Practice to build fluency with facts to 10.

Solve and practice math facts.

1 + 0	1 + 1	1 + 2	1 + 3	1 + 4	1 + 5	1 + 6	1 + 7	1 + 8	1 + 9
2 + 0	2 + 1	2 + 2	2 + 3	2 + 4	2 + 5	2 + 6	2 + 7	2 + 8	
3 + 0	3 + 1	3 + 2	3 + 3	3 + 4	3 + 5	3 + 6	3 + 7		
4 + 0	4 + 1	4 + 2	4 + 3	4+ 4	4 + 5	4 + 6			
5 + 0	5 + 1	5 + 2	5 + 3	5 + 4	5 + 5				
6 + 0	6 + 1	6 + 2	6 + 3	6 + 4					
7 + 0	7 + 1	7 + 2	7 + 3						
8 + 0	8 + 1	8 + 2							
9 + 0	9 + 1								
10 + 0									

This page intentionally left blank

Name _____   Date _____

Break the total into parts. Write a number bond and addition and subtraction number sentences to match the story.

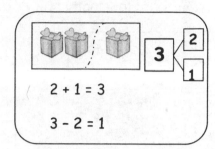

$2 + 1 = 3$

$3 - 2 = 1$

1. Rachel and Lucy are playing with 5 trucks. If Rachel is playing with 2 of them, how many is Lucy playing with?

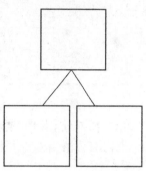

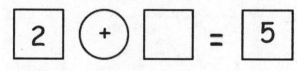

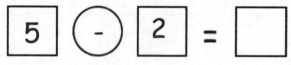

Lucy is playing with _____ trucks.

2. Jane caught 9 fish. She caught 7 fish before she ate lunch. How many fish did she catch after lunch?

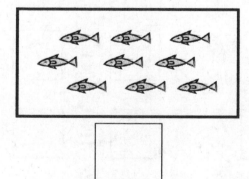

Jane caught _____ fish after lunch.

EUREKA MATH

Lesson 25:   Solve *add to with change unknown* math stories with addition, and relate to subtraction. Model with materials, and write corresponding number sentences.

119

3. Dad bought 6 shirts. The next day he returned some of them. Now, he has 2 shirts. How many shirts did Dad return?

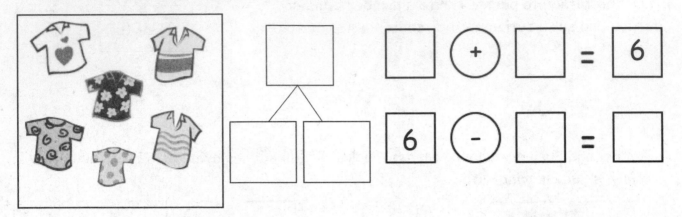

☐ + ☐ = 6

6 − ☐ = ☐

Dad returned _____ shirts.

4. John had 3 strawberries. Then, his friend gave him more fruit. Now, John has 7 pieces of fruit. How many pieces of fruit did John's friend give him?

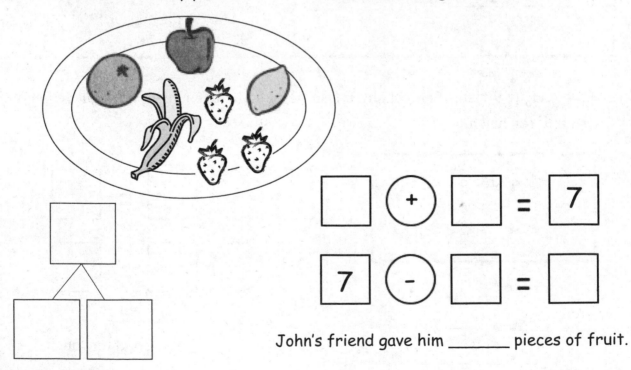

☐ + ☐ = 7

7 − ☐ = ☐

John's friend gave him _____ pieces of fruit.

Lesson 25: Solve *add to with change unknown* math stories with addition, and relate to subtraction. Model with materials, and write corresponding number sentences.

©2015 Great Minds. eureka-math.org
G1-M1-SE-B1-1.3.1-12.2015

EUREKA MATH

Name _____   Date _____

Break the total into parts. Write a number bond and addition and subtraction number sentences to match the story.

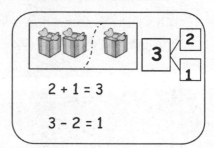

2 + 1 = 3

3 − 2 = 1

1. Six flowers bloomed on Monday. Some more bloomed on Tuesday. Now, there are 8 flowers. How many flowers bloomed on Tuesday?

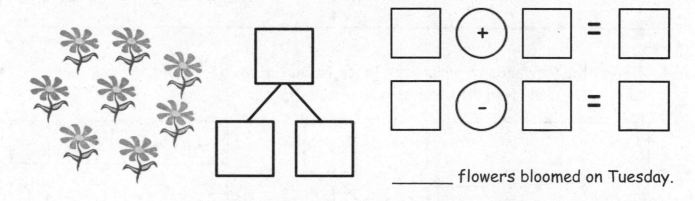

_____ flowers bloomed on Tuesday.

2. Below are the balloons that Mom bought. She bought 4 balloons for Bella, and the rest of the balloons were for Jim. How many balloons did she buy for Jim?

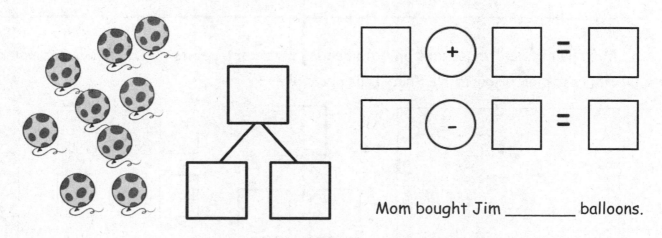

Mom bought Jim _____ balloons.

EUREKA MATH

Lesson 25: Solve *add to with change unknown* math stories with addition, and relate to subtraction. Model with materials, and write corresponding number sentences.

121

Draw a picture to solve the math story.

3. Missy buys some cupcakes and 2 cookies. Now, she has 6 desserts. How many cupcakes did she buy?

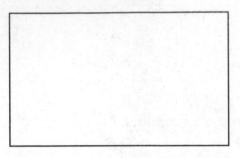
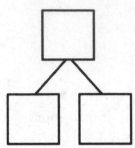
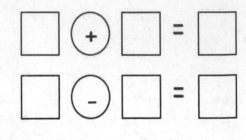

Missy bought _____ cupcakes.

4. Jim invited 9 friends to his party. Three friends arrived late, but the rest came early. How many friends came early?

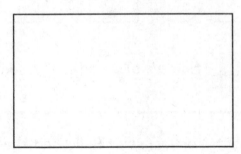
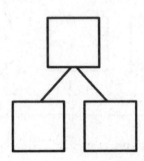
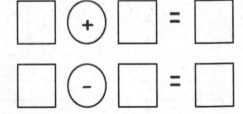

_____ friends came early.

5. Mom paints her fingernails on both hands. First, she paints 2 red. Then, she paints the rest pink. How many fingernails are pink?

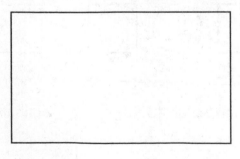
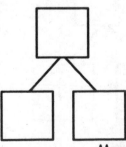

Mom paints _____ fingernails pink.

Lesson 25: Solve *add to with change unknown* math stories with addition, and relate to subtraction. Model with materials, and write corresponding number sentences.

©2015 Great Minds. eureka-math.org
G1-M1-SE-B1-1.3.1-12.2015

EUREKA
MATH™

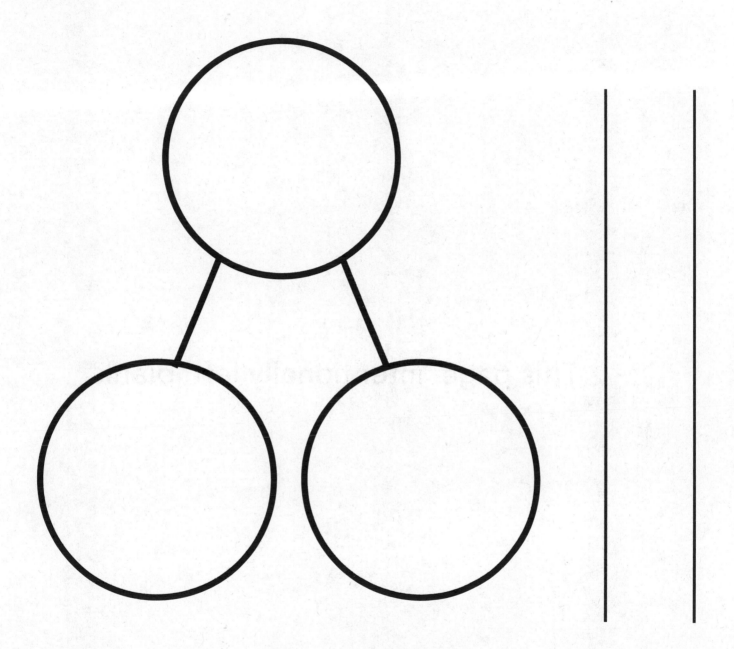

number bond and number sentences

Lesson 25: Solve *add to with change unknown* math stories with addition, and
relate to subtraction. Model with materials, and write corresponding
number sentences.

123

©2015 Great Minds. eureka-math.org
G1-M1-SE-B1-1.3.1-12.2015

This page intentionally left blank

Name _____   Date _____

Use the number path to solve.

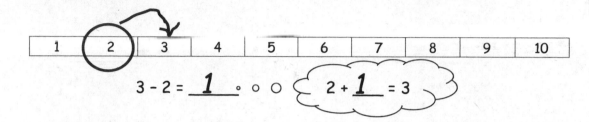

3 – 2 = __*1*__ ∘ ∘ ○   2 + __*1*__ = 3

1.

| 1 | 2 | 3 | 4 | 5 | 6 | 7 | 8 | 9 | 10 |

6 – 4 = _____ ∘∘○   4 + _____ = 6

2.

| 1 | 2 | 3 | 4 | 5 | 6 | 7 | 8 | 9 | 10 |

8 – 5 = _____ ∘○○   5 + _____ = 8

3.

| 1 | 2 | 3 | 4 | 5 | 6 | 7 | 8 | 9 | 10 |

9 – 6 = _____ ∘○○   6 + _____ = 9

4.

| 1 | 2 | 3 | 4 | 5 | 6 | 7 | 8 | 9 | 10 |

9 – 3 = _____ ∘∘○   3 + _____ = 9

EUREKA MATH™

Lesson 26:   Count on using the number path to find an unknown part.

125

Use the number path to help you solve.

| 1 | 2 | 3 | 4 | 5 | 6 | 7 | 8 | 9 | 10 |

5. $5 - 4 = $ _____ $4 + $ _____ $ = 5$

6. $5 - 1 = $ _____ $1 + $ _____ $ = 5$

7. $7 - 5 = $ _____ $5 + $ _____ $ = 7$

8. $10 - 6 = $ _____ $6 + $ _____ $ = 10$

9. $9 - 3 = $ _____ $3 + $ _____ $ = 9$

EUREKA
MATH

Name _____   Date _____

Use the number path to solve.

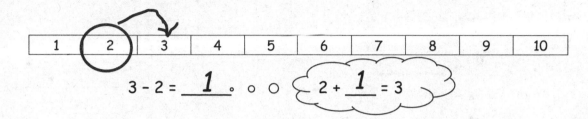

| 1 | 2 | 3 | 4 | 5 | 6 | 7 | 8 | 9 | 10 |

3 – 2 = ___*1*___ ∘ ∘ ○   2 + _*1*_ = 3

1.

| 1 | 2 | 3 | 4 | 5 | 6 | 7 | 8 | 9 | 10 |

5 – 3 = _____   ∘∘○   3 + ___ = 5

2.

| 1 | 2 | 3 | 4 | 5 | 6 | 7 | 8 | 9 | 10 |

a. 8 – 6 = ____   6 + ____ = 8

b. 7 – 4 = ____   4 + ____ = 7

c. 8 – 2 = ____   _____

d. 9 – 6 = ____   _____

EUREKA MATH™

Use the number path to solve. Match the addition sentence that can help you.

1	2	3	4	5	6	7	8	9	10

3.

a. 6 – 4 = _____

6 + 4 = 10

b. 9 – 5 = _____

10 = 7 + 3

c. 10 – 6 = _____

4 + 5 = 9

d. 10 – 7 = _____

6 = 4 + 2

4. Write an addition and subtraction number sentence for the number bond. You may use the number path to solve.

1	2	3	4	5	6	7	8	9	10

a.
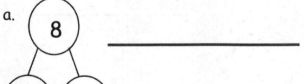

b.
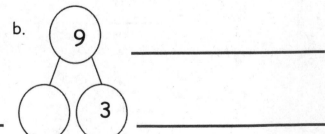

EUREKA MATH

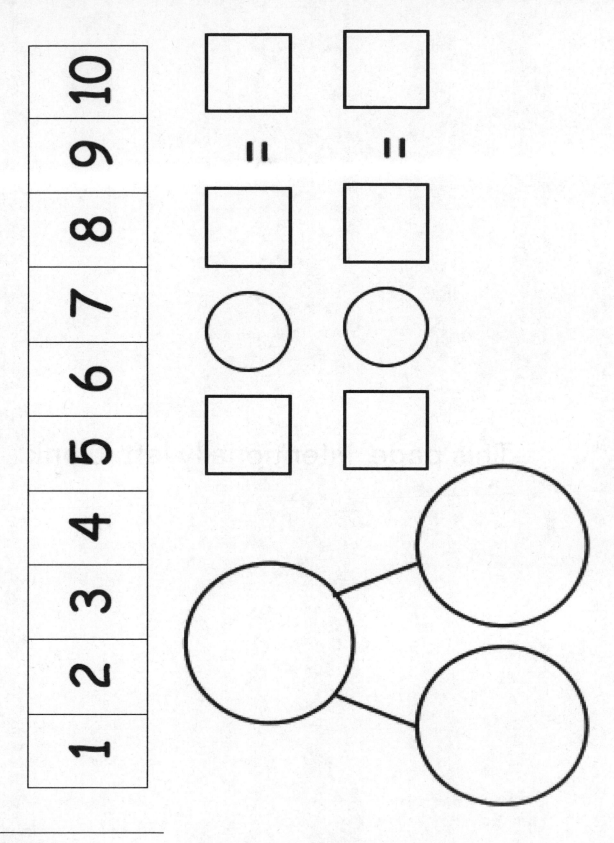

number path

EUREKA MATH

Lesson 26: Count on using the number path to find an unknown part.

129

©2015 Great Minds. eureka-math.org
G1-M1-SE-B1-1.3.1-12.2015

This page intentionally left blank

Name _____ Date _____

| 1 | 2 | 3 | 4 | 5 | 6 | 7 | 8 | 9 | 10 |

Rewrite the subtraction number sentence as an addition number sentence.

Place a ☐ around the unknown. Use the number path if you want to.

1. $4 - 3 =$ ☐   _____ + _____ = _____

2. $6 - 2 =$ ☐   _____ + _____ = _____

3. $7 - 3 =$ ☐   _____ + _____ = _____

4. $9 - 6 =$ ☐   _____

5. $10 - 2 =$ ☐   _____

Use the number path to count on.

6. $8 - 4 =$ _____ $4 +$ _____ $= 8$

7. $9 - 5 =$ _____ $5 +$ _____ $= 9$

EUREKA
MATH™

Lesson 27:   Count on using the number path to find an unknown part.

131

©2015 Great Minds. eureka-math.org
G1-M1-SE-B1-1.3.1-12.2015

| 1 | 2 | 3 | 4 | 5 | 6 | 7 | 8 | 9 | 10 |

Hop back on the number path to count back.

8. $10 - 1 =$ _____

9. $9 - 2 =$ _____

10. Pick the best way to solve the problem. Check the box.

Count on   Count back

a. $10 - 9 =$ _____   ☐   ☐

b. $9 - 1 =$ _____   ☐   ☐

c. $8 - 5 =$ _____   ☐   ☐

d. $8 - 6 =$ _____   ☐   ☐

e. $7 - 4 =$ _____   ☐   ☐

f. $6 - 3 =$ _____   ☐   ☐

EUREKA MATH™

Name _____   Date _____

Use the number path to complete the number bond, and write an addition and a subtraction sentence to match.

1.

Number Path

| 1 | 2 | 3 | 4 | 5 | 6 | 7 | 8 | 9 | 10 |

a.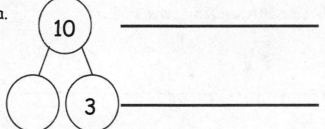

b.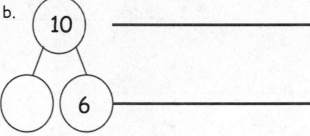

2. Solve the number sentences. Pick the best way to solve. Check the box.

Count on   Count back

a. 9 – 7 = _____   ☐   ☐

b. 8 – 2 = _____   ☐   ☐

c. 7 – 5 = _____   ☐   ☐

©2015 Great Minds. eureka-math.org
G1-M1-SE-B1-1.3.1-12.2015

3. Solve the number sentence. Pick the best way to solve. Use the number path to show why.

Count on   **Count back**

a. 7 – 5 = _____   □   □

| 1 | 2 | 3 | 4 | 5 | 6 | 7 | 8 | 9 | 10 |

I counted _____ because it needed fewer hops.

b. 9 – 1 = _____

| 1 | 2 | 3 | 4 | 5 | 6 | 7 | 8 | 9 | 10 |

I counted _____ because it needed fewer hops.

c. 10 – 8 = ____

Make a math drawing or write a number sentence to show why this is best.

EUREKA
MATH™

Name _____   Date _____

Read the story. Draw a horizontal line through the items that are leaving the story.

Then, complete the number bond, sentence, and statement.

Example: 3 – 2 = 1

1. There are 5 toy airplanes flying at the park.
    One went down and broke.
    How many airplanes are still flying?

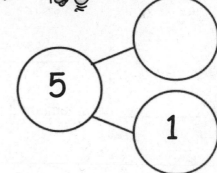

5 – 1 = _____

There are _____ airplanes still flying.

2. I had 6 eggs from the store.
    Three of them were cracked.
    How many eggs did I have that were not cracked?

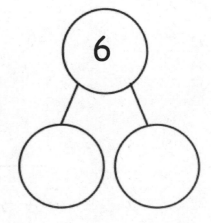

6 – ____ = _____

_____ eggs were not cracked.

EUREKA
MATH™

Lesson 28:   Solve *take from with result unknown* math stories with math drawings,
              true number sentences, and statements, using horizontal marks to
              cross off what is taken away.

135

Draw a number bond and math drawing to help you solve the problems.

3. Kate saw 8 cats playing in the grass.
    Three went away to chase a mouse.
    How many cats remained in the grass?

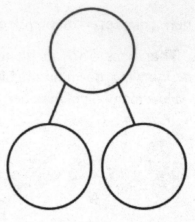

$$\underline{\hspace{2cm}} - \underline{\hspace{2cm}} = \underline{\hspace{2cm}}$$

_____ cats remained in the grass.

4. There were 7 mango slices.
    Two of them were eaten.
    How many mango slices are left to eat?

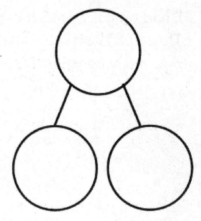

$$\underline{\hspace{2cm}} - \underline{\hspace{2cm}} = \underline{\hspace{2cm}}$$

There are _____ mango slices left.

Lesson 28:   Solve *take from with result unknown* math stories with math drawings, true number sentences, and statements, using horizontal marks to cross off what is taken away.

©2015 Great Minds. eureka-math.org
G1-M1-SE-B1-1.3.1-12.2015

EUREKA
MATH™

Name _____   Date _____

Read the story. Make a math drawing to solve.

Sample: 3-2=1

1. There were 6 hot dogs on the grill. Two finish cooking and are removed. How many hot dogs remain on the grill?

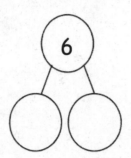

6 - ___ = ___

There are ____ hot dogs remaining on the grill.

2. Bob buys 8 new toy cars. He takes 3 out of the bag. How many cars are still in the bag?

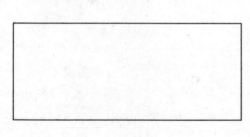
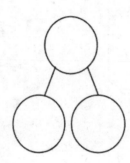

___ - ___ = ___

____ cars are still in the bag.

3. Kira sees 7 birds in the tree. Three birds fly away. How many birds are still in the tree?

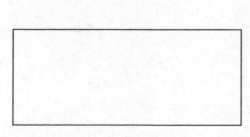

___ - ___ = ___

____ birds are still in the tree.

Lesson 28:   Solve *take from with result unknown* math stories with math drawings, true number sentences, and statements, using horizontal marks to cross off what is taken away.

4. Brad has 9 friends over for a party. Six friends get picked up. How many friends are still at the party?

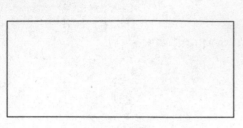

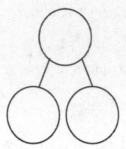

_____ - _____ = _____

_____ friends are still
at the party.

5. Jordan was playing with 10 cars. He gave 7 to Kate.
    How many cars is Jordan playing with now?

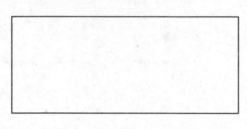

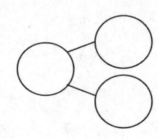

_____ - _____ = _____

Jordan is playing
with _____ cars now.

6. Tony takes 4 books from the bookshelf. There were 10 books on the shelf to start.
    How many books are on the shelf now?

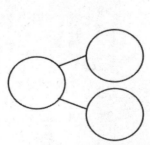

_____ - _____ = _____

_____ books are
on the shelf now.

Lesson 28:   Solve *take from with result unknown* math stories with math drawings,
                                true number sentences, and statements, using horizontal marks to
                                cross off what is taken away.

EUREKA
MATH™

Name _____ Date _____

Complete the story and solve. Label the number bond.
Color the missing part in the number sentence and number bond.

1. There are _____ apples.

    _____ have worms. Yuck!

    How many good apples are there?

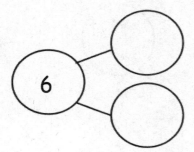

$$6 \; - \; \boxed{} \; = \; \boxed{}$$

There are _____ good apples.

2. _____ books are in the case.

    _____ books are on the top shelf.

    How many books are on the bottom shelf?

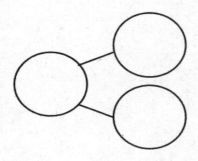

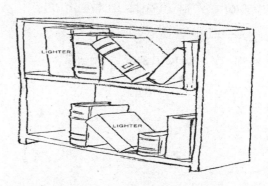

$$9 \; - \; \boxed{} \; = \; \boxed{}$$

_____ books are on the bottom shelf.

EUREKA MATH

Lesson 29: Solve *take apart with addend unknown* math stories with math drawings, equations, and statements, circling the known part to find the unknown.

139

©2015 Great Minds. eureka-math.org
G1-M1-SE-B1-1.3.1-12.2015

Use number bonds and math drawings in a line to solve.

Example of math drawing and number sentence

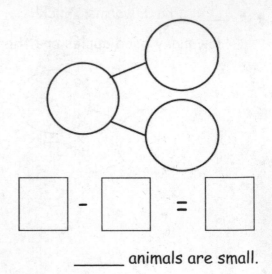

$5 - 4 = 1$

3. There are 8 animals at the pond.
    Two are big. The rest are small.
    How many are small?

☐ − ☐ = ☐

_____ animals are small.

4. There are 7 students in the class.
    _____ students are girls.
    How many students are boys?

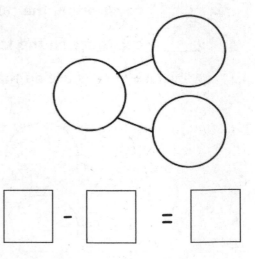

☐ − ☐ = ☐

_____ students are boys.

Lesson 29:   Solve *take apart with addend unknown* math stories with math drawings, equations, and statements, circling the known part to find the unknown.

©2015 Great Minds. eureka-math.org
G1-M1-SE-B1-1.3.1-12.2015

EUREKA
MATH

Name _____   Date _____

Read the math stories. Make math drawings to solve.    $5 - 4 = 1$

1. Tom has a box of 7 crayons. Five crayons are red. How many crayons are not red?

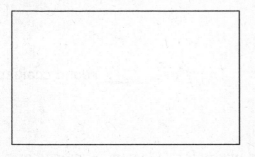   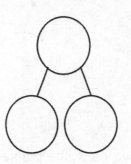

_____ - _____ = _____

_____ crayons are not red.

2. Mary picks 8 flowers. Two are daisies. The rest are tulips. How many tulips does she pick?

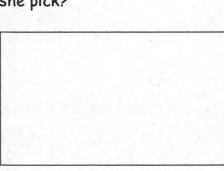   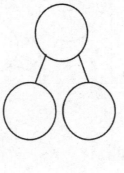

_____ - _____ = _____

Mary picks _____ tulips.

3. There are 9 pieces of fruit in the bowl. Four are apples. The rest are oranges. How many pieces of fruit are oranges?

_____ - _____ = _____

The bowl has _____ oranges.

EUREKA MATH

Lesson 29:   Solve *take apart with addend unknown* math stories with math drawings, equations, and statements, circling the known part to find the unknown.

141

©2015 Great Minds. eureka-math.org
G1-M1-SE-B1-1.3.1-12.2015

4. Mom and Ben make 10 cookies. Six are stars. The rest are round. How many cookies are round?

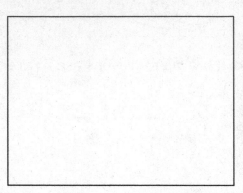   

____ - ____ = ____

There are _____ round cookies.

5. The parking lot has 7 spaces. Two cars are parked in the lot. How many more cars can park in the lot?

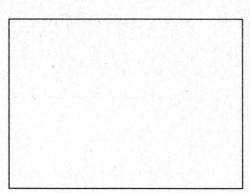   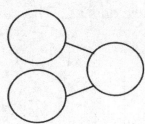

____ - ____ = ____

_____ more cars can park in the lot.

6. Liz has 2 fingers with Band Aids. How many fingers are not hurt?

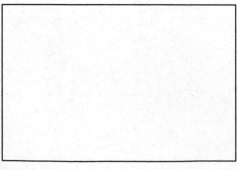   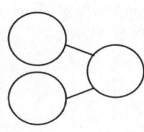

____ - ____ = ____

Write a statement for your answer:

_____

Lesson 29:   Solve *take apart with addend unknown* math stories with math drawings, equations, and statements, circling the known part to find the unknown.

©2015 Great Minds. eureka-math.org
G1-M1-SE-B1-1.3.1-12.2015

EUREKA MATH

Name _____ Date _____

Solve the math stories. Complete and label the number bond and the picture number bond.   Lightly shade in the solution.

1. Jill was given a total of 5 flowers for her birthday. She put 3 in one vase and the rest in another vase. How many flowers did she put in the other vase?

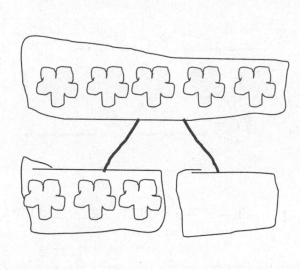

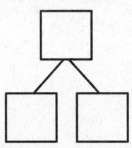

$3 \; \bigoplus \; \square \; = \; 5$

$5 \; \bigominus \; 3 \; = \; \square$

2. Kate and Nana were baking cookies. They made 5 heart-shaped cookies and then made some square cookies. They made 8 cookies altogether. How many square cookies did they make? Draw and solve.

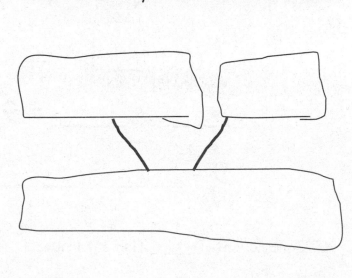

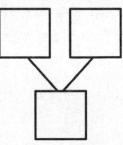

$5 \; \bigoplus \; \square \; = \; 8$

$8 \; \bigominus \; 5 \; = \; \square$

EUREKA MATH™

Lesson 30:   Solve *add to with change unknown* math stories with drawings, relating addition and subtraction.

143

Solve. Complete and label the number bond and the picture number bond. Circle the unknown number.

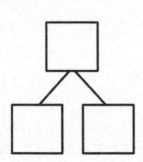

3. Bill has 2 trucks. His friend James came over with some more.
   Together, they have 6 trucks.
   How many trucks did James bring over?

_____ + _____ = 6

6 - _____ = _____

James brought over _____ trucks.

---

4. Jane caught 5 fish before she stopped to eat lunch.
   After lunch, she caught some more.
   At the end of the day, she had 9 fish.
   How many fish did she catch after lunch?

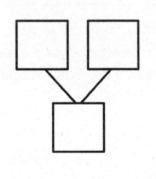

_____ + _____ = 9

9 - _____ = _____

Jane caught _____ fish after lunch.

Lesson 30: Solve *add to with change unknown* math stories with drawings, relating addition and subtraction.

©2015 Great Minds. eureka-math.org
G1-M1-SE-B1-1.3.1-12.2015

EUREKA MATH

Name _____ Date _____

Solve the math stories. Draw and label a picture number bond to solve. Circle the unknown number.

1. Grace has a total of 7 dolls. She puts 2 in the toy box and takes the rest to her friend's house. How many dolls does she take to her friend's house?

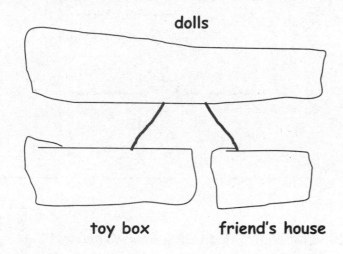

dolls

toy box   friend's house

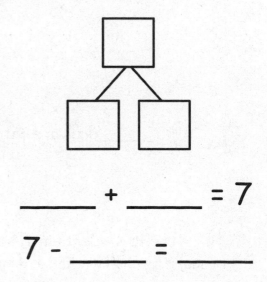

_____ + _____ = 7

7 - _____ = _____

Grace takes _____ dolls to her friend's house.

2. Jack can invite 8 friends to his birthday party. He makes 3 invitations. How many invitations does he still need to make?

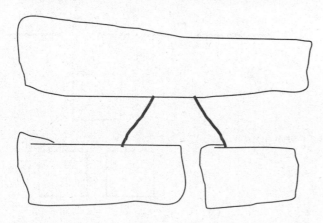

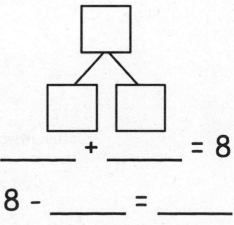

_____ + _____ = 8

8 - _____ = _____

Jack still needs to make _____ invitations.

EUREKA MATH

Lesson 30: Solve *add to with change unknown* math stories with drawings, relating addition and subtraction.

145

©2015 Great Minds. eureka-math.org
G1-M1-SE-B1-1.3.1-12.2015

3. There are 9 dogs at the park. Five dogs play with balls. The rest are eating bones.
   How many dogs are eating bones?

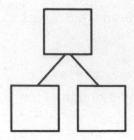

_____ + _____ = 9

_____ dogs are eating bones.

_____ - _____ = _____

4. There are 10 students in Jim's class. Seven bought lunch at school. The rest
   brought lunch from home. How many students brought lunch from home?

_____ + _____ = _____

_____ - _____ = _____

_____ students brought lunch from home.

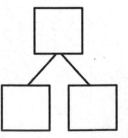

Lesson 30:   Solve *add to with change unknown* math stories with drawings,
                    relating addition and subtraction.

EUREKA
MATH™

Name _____ Date _____

Make a math drawing, and circle the part you know. Cross out the unknown part.

Complete the number sentence and number bond.

Sample: 3 – 1 = 2

1. Kate made 7 cookies. Bill ate some. Now, Kate has 5 cookies.
    How many cookies did Bill eat?

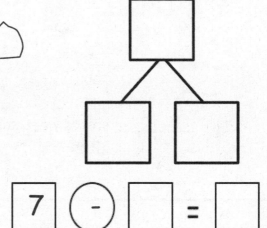

$$7 \;-\; \square \;=\; \square$$

Bill ate _____ cookies.

2. On Monday, Tim had 8 pencils. On Tuesday, he lost some pencils.
    On Wednesday, he has 4 pencils. How many pencils did Tim lose?

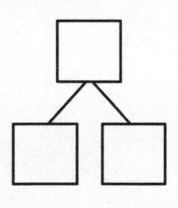

Tim lost _____ pencils.

$$\square \;-\; \square \;=\; \square$$

EUREKA MATH

Lesson 31: Solve *take from with change unknown* math stories with drawings.

147

©2015 Great Minds. eureka-math.org
G1-M1-SE-B1-1.3.1-12.2015

3. A store had 6 shirts on the rack. Now, there are 2 shirts on the rack.
   How many shirts were sold?

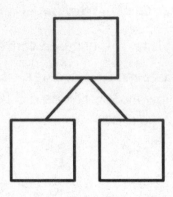

_____ shirts were sold.

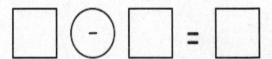

---

4. There were 9 children at the park. Some children went inside. Five children stayed.
   How many children went inside?

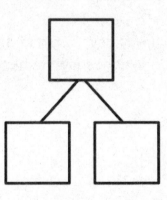

_____ children went inside.

Lesson 31:   Solve *take from with change unknown* math stories with drawings.

EUREKA
MATH

Name _____   Date _____

Make a math drawing, and circle the part you know.
Cross out the unknown part.
Complete the number sentence and number bond.

Sample 3 - 1 = 2

1. Missy gets 6 presents for her birthday. She unwraps some. Four are still wrapped. How many presents did she unwrap?

   Missy unwrapped _____ presents.

   $6 - \square = \square$

2. Ann has a box of 8 markers. Some fall on the floor. Six are still in the box. How many markers fell on the floor?

   _____ markers fell on the floor.

   $\square - \square = \square$

3. Nick makes 7 cupcakes for his friends. Some cupcakes were eaten. Now, there are 5 left. How many cupcakes were eaten?

   _____ cupcakes were eaten.

   $\square - \square = \square$

EUREKA MATH

Lesson 31:   Solve *take from with change unknown* math stories with drawings.

149

©2015 Great Minds. eureka-math.org
G1-M1-SE-B1-1.3.1-12.2015

4. A dog has 8 bones. He hides some. He still has 5 bones. How many bones are hidden?

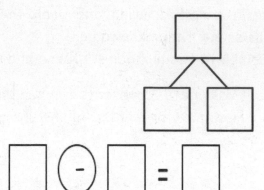

_____ bones are hidden.

5. The cafeteria table can seat 10 students. Some of the seats are taken. Seven seats are empty. How many seats are taken?

_____ seats are taken.

6. Ron has 10 sticks of gum. He gives one stick to each of his friends. Now, he has 3 sticks of gum left. How many friends did Ron share with?

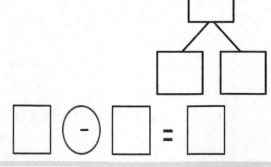

Ron shared with _____ friends.

Lesson 31:   Solve *take from with change unknown* math stories with drawings.

EUREKA MATH

Name _____ Date _____

Solve. Use simple math drawings to show how to solve with addition and subtraction. Label the number bond.

1.

There are 5 apples.
Four are Sam's.
The rest are Jim's.
How many apples does Jim have?

Jim has _____ apple.

2.

There are 8 mushrooms. Five are black. The rest are white.
How many mushrooms are white?

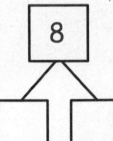

_____ mushrooms are white.

EUREKA MATH

Lesson 32:   Solve *put together/take apart with addend unknown* math stories.

151

Use the number bond to complete the number sentences. Use simple math drawings to tell math stories.

3.

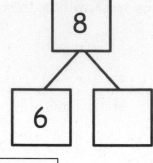

_____ + _____ = 8

8 - _____ = _____

4.

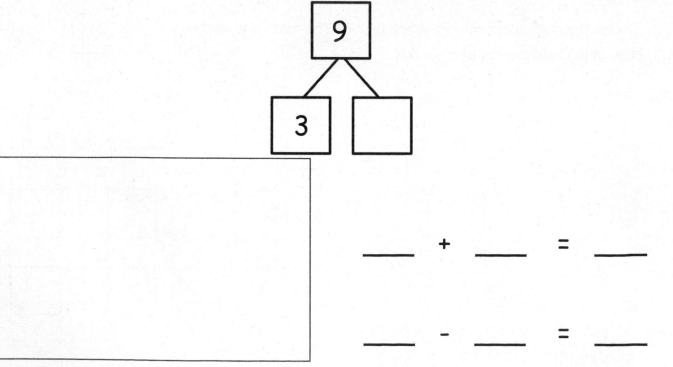

_____ + _____ = _____

_____ - _____ = _____

Lesson 32:   Solve *put together/take apart with addend unknown* math stories.

EUREKA
MATH

Name _____ Date _____

Match the math stories to the number sentences that tell the story. Make a math drawing to solve.

1. a.

There are 10 flowers in a vase.	
6 are red.	
The rest are yellow.	
How many flowers are yellow?	

☐ (+) ☐ = 9

9 (−) ☐ = ☐

b.

There are 9 apples in a basket.
6 are red.
The rest are green.
How many apples are green?

3 (+) ☐ = 10

10 (−) ☐ = ☐

c.

Kate has her fingernails painted.
3 have designs.
The rest are plain.
How many fingernails are plain?

6 (+) ☐ = 10

10 (−) 6 = ☐

EUREKA
MATH™

Lesson 32: Solve *put together/take apart with addend unknown* math stories.

153

Use the number bond to tell an addition and subtraction math story with pictures. Write an addition and subtraction number sentence.

2.

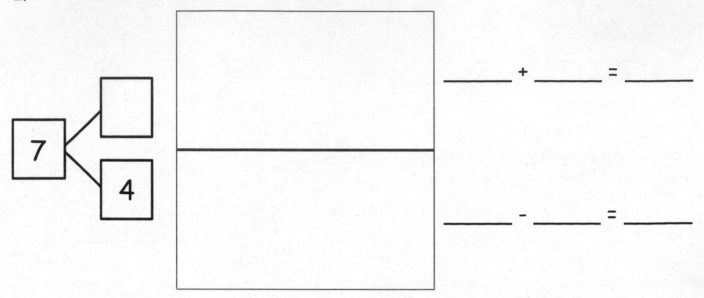

___ + ___ = ___

___ - ___ = ___

3.

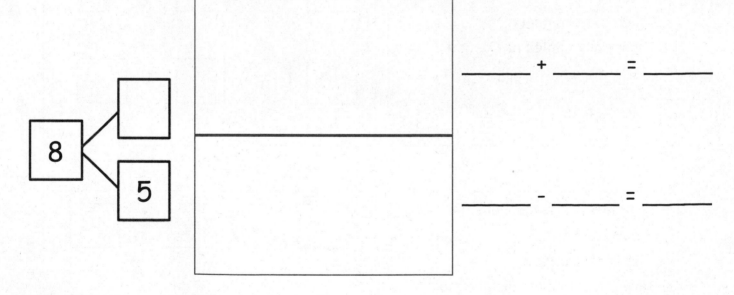

___ + ___ = ___

___ - ___ = ___

    Lesson 32:   Solve *put together/take apart with addend unknown* math stories.

EUREKA MATH

Name _____ Date _____

Cross off, when needed, to subtract.

1.

    6 – 1 = ___

2.

    6 – 0 = ___

If you want, make a 5-group drawing for each problem like the ones above.
Show the subtraction.

3.

    7 – 1 = ___

4.

    7 – 0 = ___

5.

    10 – 1 = ___

6.

    10 – 0 = ___

7.

    8 – 1 = ___

8.

    8 – 0 = ___

9.

    9 – 1 = ___

10.

    9 – 0 = ___

EUREKA MATH

Lesson 33: Model 0 less and 1 less pictorially and as subtraction number
sentences.

155

Cross off, when needed, to subtract.

11.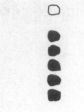

6 – 1 = ____

12.

8 – 1 = ____

13.

9 – 0 = ____

Subtract.

14.   7 – 1 = ____

15.   8 – 0 = ____

16.   9 – 1 = ____

17.   Fill in the missing number.   Visualize your 5-groups to help you.

a. 6 – 0 = ____

b. 6 – 1 = ____

c. 7 – ____ = 7

d. 7 – 1 = ____

e. 8 – 0 = ____

f. 8 – ____ = 7

g. 9 – ____ = 9

h. 9 – 1 = ____

i. 10 – ____ = 10

j. 10 – ____ = 9

Lesson 33:   Model 0 less and 1 less pictorially and as subtraction number sentences.

EUREKA MATH

Name _____   Date _____

Show the subtraction. If you want, use a 5-group drawing for each problem.

8-1 = 7

1.

$$9 - 1 = \underline{\quad}$$

2.

$$9 - 0 = \underline{\quad}$$

3.

$$6 - \underline{\quad} = 6$$

4.

$$6 = 7 - \underline{\quad}$$

Show the subtraction. If you want, use a 5-group drawing like the model for each problem.

9-1 = 8

5.

$$9 - \underline{\quad} = 9$$

6.

$$8 = 8 - \underline{\quad}$$

7.

$$10 - \underline{\quad} = 9$$

8.

$$7 - \underline{\quad} = 7$$

EUREKA MATH

Lesson 33:   Model 0 less and 1 less pictorially and as subtraction number sentences.

157

Write the subtraction number sentence to match the 5-group drawing.

9.

____ - ____ = ____

10. ●●●● ○ ○

____ - ____ = ____

11.

____ - ____ = ____

12.

____ - ____ = ____

13.

____ - ____ = ____

14. Fill in the missing number. Visualize your 5-groups to help you.

a. 7 – ____ = 6

b. 0 = 7 – ____

c. 8 – ____ = 7

d. 6 – ____ = 5

e. 8 = 9 – ____

f. 9 = 10 – ____

g. 10 – ____ = 10

h. 9 – ____ = 8

Lesson 33:   Model 0 less and 1 less pictorially and as subtraction number sentences.

©2015 Great Minds. eureka-math.org
G1-M1-SE-B1-1.3.1-12.2015

EUREKA MATH™

Name _____ Date _____

Cross off to subtract.

8-7 = _!_

1. ●●●●● ○

6 – 6 = ___

2. ●●●●● ○

6 – 5 = ___

Subtract. Make a math drawing, like those above, for each.

3.

7 – 7 = ___

4.

7 – 6 = ___

5.

10 – 10 = ___

6.

10 – 9 = ___

7.

8 – 8 = ___

8.

8 – 7 = ___

9.

9 – 9 = ___

10.

9 – 8 = ___

Lesson 34:   Model $n - n$ and $n - (n - 1)$ pictorially and as subtraction sentences.

159

EUREKA
MATH™

Cross off, when needed, to subtract.

11.

     6 – 6 = _____

12.

     8 – 8 = _____

13.

     9 – 8 = _____

Subtract. Make a math drawing, like those above, for each.

14.

     7 – 7 = _____

15.

     8 – 7 = _____

16.

     9 – 9 = _____

17. Fill in the missing number. Visualize your 5-groups to help you.

    a.   6 – 6 = _____   b.   6 – 5 = _____

    c.   7 – _____ = 0   d.   7 – 6 = _____

    e.   8 – 8 = _____   f.   8 – _____ = 1

    g.   9 – _____ = 0   h.   9 – 8 = _____

    i.   10 – _____ = 10   j.   10 – _____ = 1

Lesson 34:   Model $n - n$ and $n - (n - 1)$ pictorially and as subtraction sentences.

EUREKA MATH™

©2015 Great Minds. eureka-math.org
G1-M1-SE-B1-1.3.1-12.2015

Name _____   Date _____

Cross off to subtract.

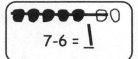

$7-6 = \underline{1}$

1. ⬤⬤⬤⬤⬤ ⬭⬭⬭⬭⬭

       $10 - 10 = \underline{\hspace{1.5cm}}$

2. ⬤⬤⬤⬤⬤ ⬭⬭⬭⬭

       $9 - 8 = \underline{\hspace{1.5cm}}$

Make a 5-group drawing like those above. Show the subtraction.

3.

      $1 = \underline{\hspace{1cm}} - 7$

4.

      $8 - \underline{\hspace{1cm}} = 0$

5.

      $0 = \underline{\hspace{1cm}} - 7$

6.

      $6 - \underline{\hspace{1cm}} = 1$

Make a 5-group drawing like the model for each problem. Show the subtraction.

7.

      $9 - \underline{\hspace{1cm}} = 1$

8.

      $0 = 8 - \underline{\hspace{1cm}}$

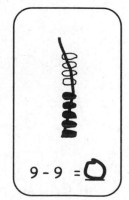

$9 - 9 = 0$

Write the subtraction number sentence to match the 5-group drawing.

9. ●●●●● ○ ○   10. ●●●●● ○○○○   11. ●●●●● ○ ○ ○

___ - ___ = ___   ___ - ___ = ___   ___ - ___ = ___

12.    13.

___ - ___ = ___   ___ - ___ = ___

14. Fill in the missing number. Visualize your 5-groups to help you.

a. 7 – ___ = 0   b. 1 = 7 – ___

c. 8 – ___ = 1   d. 6 – ___ = 0

e. 0 = 9 – ___   f. 1 = 10 – ___

g. 10 - ___ = 0   h. 9 – ___ = 1

162   Lesson 34:   Model n − n and n − (n − 1) pictorially and as subtraction sentences.

EUREKA
MATH

Name _____   Date _____

Solve the sets of number sentences. Look for easy groups to cross off.

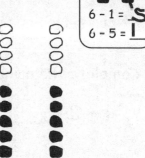

6 – 1 = _S_

6 – 5 = _I_

1.

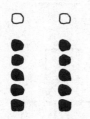

6 – 5 = ___

6 – 1 = ___

2.

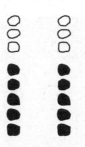

8 – 3 = ___

8 – 5 = ___

3.

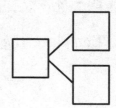

9 – 4 = ___

9 – 5 = ___

Subtract. Make a math drawing for each problem like the ones above. Write a number bond.

4.

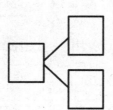

7 – 5 = ___

7 – 2 = ___

5.

10 – 5 = ___

Lesson 35:   Relate subtraction facts involving fives and doubles to corresponding decompositions.

163

©2015 Great Minds. eureka-math.org
G1-M1-SE-B1-1.3.1-12.2015

6. Solve. Visualize your 5-groups to help you.

   a. 7 – 5 = ____   b. 7 – ____ = 5   c. 8 – 3 = ____

   d. 9 – ____ = 4   e. 9 – ____ = 5   f. 8 – ____ = 3

Complete the number bond and number sentence for each problem.

7. 4 – 2 = ____

8. 6 – 3 = ____

9. 10 – 5 = ____

10. 8 – 4 = ____
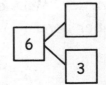

11. 8 – 4 = ____

12. 6 – 3 = ____

13. Complete the number sentences below. Circle the strategy that can help.

   a.   7 – 5 = ____   5-groups   doubles

   b.   7 – 2 = ____   5-groups   doubles

   c.   8 – 4 = ____   5-groups   doubles

   d.   8 – 3 = ____   5-groups   doubles

   e.   8 – 5 = ____   5-groups   doubles

   f.   10 – 5 = ____   5-groups   doubles

Lesson 35:   Relate subtraction facts involving fives and doubles to corresponding
                 decompositions.

EUREKA
MATH

Name _____ Date _____

Solve the sets of number sentences. Look for easy groups to cross off.

1.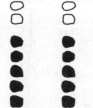

7 – 5 = _____

7 – 2 = _____

2.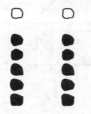

6 – 5 = ____

6 – 1 = ____

3.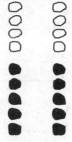

9 – ____ = 4

9 – ____ = 5

6 – 1 = ____

6 – 5 = ____

Subtract. Make a math drawing for each problem like the ones above. Write a number bond.

4.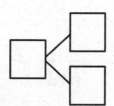

10 – 5 = _____

5.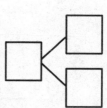

8 – 5 = ____

8 – ____ = 5

6. Solve. Visualize 5-groups to help you.

a. 9 – ____ = 4   b. ____ – 5 = 5   c. 8 – ____ = 5

d. ____ – 5 = 2   e. ____ – 5 = 3   f. ____ – 4 = 5

Lesson 35: Relate subtraction facts involving fives and doubles to corresponding decompositions.

165

Complete the number sentence and number bond for each problem.

7.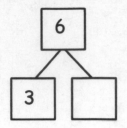

6 – 3 = ___

8.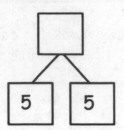

___ – 5 = 5

9.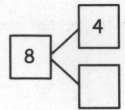

8 – ___ = 4

10. Match the number sentence to the strategy that helps you solve.

a. 7 – ___ = 2

	doubles

b. 8 – ___ = 3

●●●●● ○○○○○	5-groups

c. 10 – ___ = 5

●●●●● ○○○○○	5-groups

d. ___ – 3 = 3

	doubles

e. 8 – ___ = 4

●●●●● ○○○○○	5-groups

f. 9 – ___ = 5

	doubles

Lesson 35:   Relate subtraction facts involving fives and doubles to corresponding decompositions.

©2015 Great Minds. eureka-math.org
G1-M1-SE-B1-1.3.1-12.2015

EUREKA
MATH™

Name _____   Date _____

Solve the sets. Cross off on the 5-groups.
Use the first number sentence to help you solve the next.

1.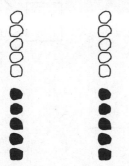

10 – 9 = ___

10 – 1 = ___

2.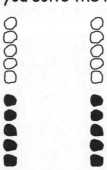

10 – 6 = ___

10 – 4 = ___

3.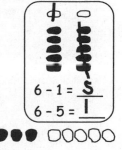

6 – 1 = __5__
6 – 5 = __1__

10 – 3 = ___

10 – 7 = ___

Make a math drawing and solve.

4.

10 – 4 = ___

10 – 6 = ___

5.

10 – 5 = ___

6.

10 – 8 = ___

10 – 2 = ___

Subtract. Then, write the related subtraction sentence.
Make a math drawing if needed, and complete a number bond for each.

7.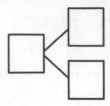

$10 - 8 =$ _____

_____

8.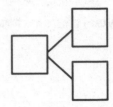

$10 - 9 =$ _____

_____

9.

$10 - 3 =$ _____

_____

10.

$10 - 6 =$ _____

_____

11. Fill in the missing part. Write the 2 matching subtraction sentences.

a.
_____

_____

b.
_____

_____

c.
_____

_____

d.
_____

_____

e.
_____

_____

Lesson 36:   Relate subtraction from 10 to corresponding decompositions.   **EUREKA MATH**

Name _____   Date _____

Make a math drawing, and solve. Use the first number sentence to help you write a related number sentence that matches your picture.

1.   2.   3.

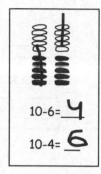

10-6= 4

10-4= 6

10 – 2 = _____   10 – 1 = _____   10 – 7 = _____

__ - __ = __   __ - __ = ___   __ - __ = __

Subtract. Then, write the related subtraction sentence. Make a math drawing if needed, and complete a number bond for each.

4. 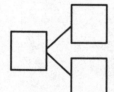   5. 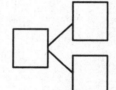   6.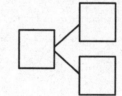

10 – 2 = ___   10 – __ = 9   10 - ___ = 6

_____   _____   _____

7. 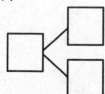   10 – ___ = 1   8.    ___ = 10 - 5

_____   _____

9. Complete the number bond. Match the number bond to the related subtraction sentence. Write the other related subtraction number sentence.

a.

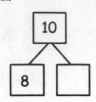

10 – 5 = ___   ___ - ___ = ___

b.

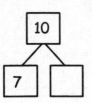

10 – 1 = ___   ___ - ___ = ___

c.

10 - 2 = ___   ___ - ___ = ___

d.

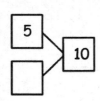

10 – 4 = ___   ___ - ___ = ___

e.

10 – 3 = ___   ___ - ___ = ___

©2015 Great Minds. eureka-math.org
G1-M1-SE-B1-1.3.1-12.2015

Name _____   Date _____

Solve the sets. Cross off on the 5-groups. Write the related subtraction sentence that would have the same number bond.

1.
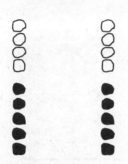

9 – 8 = ___

9 – 1 = ___

2.
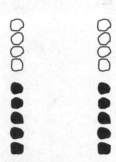

9 – 7 = ___

_____

3.

9 – 9 = ___

_____

Make a 5-group drawing. Solve, and write a related subtraction sentence that would have the same number bond. Cross off to show.

4.

9 – 6 = ___

_____

5.

9 – 4 = ___

_____

6.

9 – 3 = ___

_____

Subtract. Then, write the related subtraction sentence.
Make a math drawing if needed, and complete a number bond.

7.

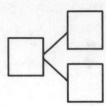

$9 - 5 =$ _____

_____

8.

$9 - 8 =$ _____

_____

9.

$9 - 7 =$ _____

_____

10.

$9 - 3 =$ _____

_____

11. Fill in the missing part. Write the 2 matching subtraction sentences.

a.

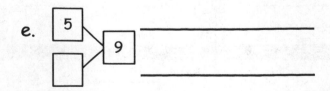

9 / 0 / ☐ _____ _____

b.

8 / 9 / ☐ _____ _____

c.

9 / 2 / ☐ _____ _____

d.

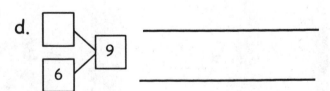

☐ / 6 / 9 _____ _____

e.

5 / 9 / ☐ _____ _____

EUREKA MATH

Name _____   Date _____

Make 5-group drawings and solve. Use the first number sentence to help
you write a related number sentence that matches your picture.

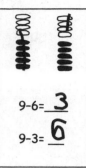

$9-6=\underline{3}$

$9-3=\underline{6}$

1.   2.   3.

$9 - 2 = \underline{}$ $9 - 8 = \underline{}$ $9 - 4 = \underline{}$

$\underline{} - \underline{} = \underline{}$ $\underline{} - \underline{} = \underline{}$ $\underline{} - \underline{} = \underline{}$

Subtract. Then, write the related subtraction sentence. Make a math drawing if
needed, and complete a number bond for each.

4. 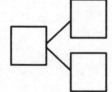   5. 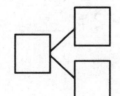   6.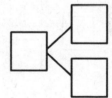

$9 - 7 = \underline{}$ $9 - \underline{} = 9$ $9 - \underline{} = 6$

_____   _____   _____

7. 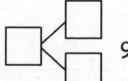 $9 - \underline{} = 1$ 8.  $\underline{} = 9 - 5$

_____   _____

9. Use 5-group drawings to help you complete the number bond. Match the number bond to the related subtraction sentence. Write the other related subtraction number sentence.

a.

$9 - 5 =$ ___   ___ $-$ ___ $=$ ___

b.

$9 - 1 =$ ____   ___ $-$ ___ $=$ ___

c.

$9 - 2 =$ ____   ___ $-$ ___ $=$ ___

d.

$9 - 6 =$ ___   ___ $-$ ___ $=$ ___

e.

$9 -$ ___ $= 0$ ___ $-$ ___ $=$ ___

EUREKA MATH

Name _____   Date _____

1+9									
1+8	2+8								
1+7	2+7	3+7							
1+6	2+6	3+6	4+6						
1+5	2+5	3+5	4+5	5+5					
1+4	2+4	3+4	4+4	5+4	6+4				
1+3	2+3	3+3	4+3	5+3	6+3	7+3			
1+2	2+2	3+2	4+2	5+2	6+2	7+2	8+2		
1+1	2+1	3+1	4+1	5+1	6+1	7+1	8+1	9+1	
1+0	2+0	3+0	4+0	5+0	6+0	7+0	8+0	9+0	10+0

6 – 4

Pick a subtraction card.

Find the related addition fact on the chart and shade it in.

Write the subtraction sentence and a number bond to match.

Continue for at least 6 turns.

Lesson 38:   Look for and make use of repeated reasoning and structure using the addition chart to solve subtraction problems.

175

This page intentionally left blank

On your addition chart, shade a square orange. Write the related subtraction fact in a space below with its number bond. Color all the totals orange.

1. _____ - _____ = _____

2. _____ - _____ = _____

3. _____ - _____ = _____

4. _____ = _____ - _____

5. _____ = _____ - _____

EUREKA MATH

Lesson 38: Look for and make use of repeated reasoning and structure using the addition chart to solve subtraction problems.

177

©2015 Great Minds. eureka-math.org
G1-M1-SE-B1-1.3.1-12.2015

This page intentionally left blank

Name _____ Date _____

Find and solve the 7 unshaded addition problems that are doubles and 5-groups.

Make subtraction flashcards for the related subtraction facts. (Remember, doubles will only make 1 related subtraction fact instead of 2 related facts.)

Make a number bond card and use your cards to play Memory.

1 + 0	1 + 1	1 + 2	1 + 3	1 + 4	1 + 5	1 + 6	1 + 7	1 + 8	1 + 9
2 + 0	2 + 1	2 + 2	2 + 3	2 + 4	2 + 5	2 + 6	2 + 7	2 + 8	
3 + 0	3 + 1	3 + 2	3 + 3	3 + 4	3 + 5	3 + 6	3 + 7		
4 + 0	4 + 1	4 + 2	4 + 3	4 + 4	4 + 5	4 + 6			
5 + 0	5 + 1	5 + 2	5 + 3	5 + 4	5 + 5				
6 + 0	6 + 1	6 + 2	6 + 3	6 + 4					
7 + 0	7 + 1	7 + 2	7 + 3						
8 + 0	8 + 1	8 + 2							
9 + 0	9 + 1								
10 + 0									

EUREKA MATH™

Lesson 38: Look for and make use of repeated reasoning and structure using the addition chart to solve subtraction problems.

179

This page intentionally left blank

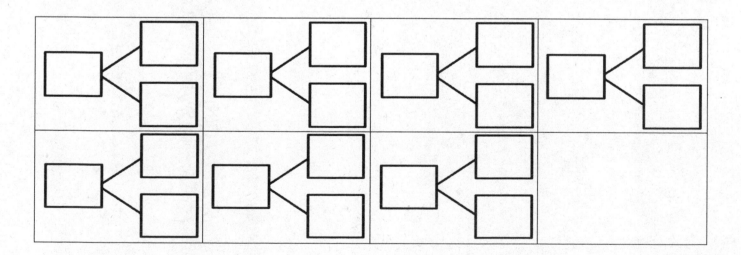

EUREKA MATH

Lesson 38: Look for and make use of repeated reasoning and structure using the addition chart to solve subtraction problems.

181

©2015 Great Minds. eureka-math.org
G1-M1-SE-B1-1.3.1-12.2015

This page intentionally left blank

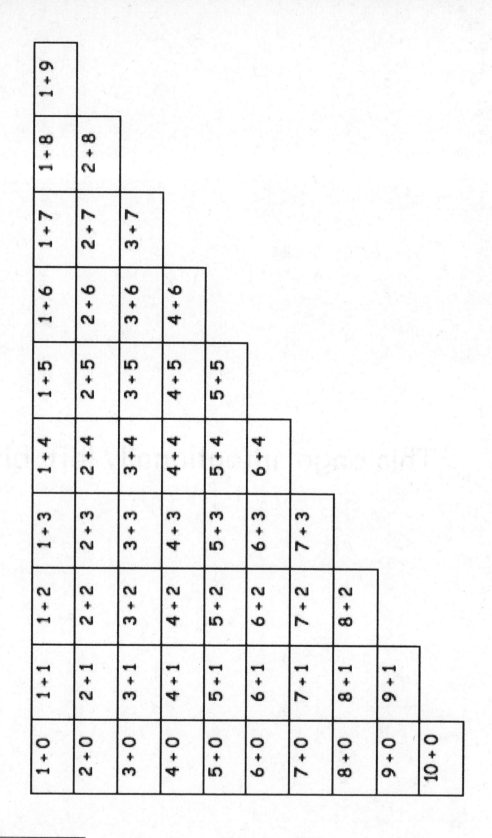

addition chart - from Lesson 21

Lesson 38:   Look for and make use of repeated reasoning and structure using the addition chart to solve subtraction problems.

This page intentionally left blank

Name _____ Date _____

Study the addition chart to solve and write related problems.

1+9									
1+8	2+8								
1+7	2+7	3+7							
1+6	2+6	3+6	4+6						
1+5	2+5	3+5	4+5	5+5					
1+4	2+4	3+4	4+4	5+4	6+4				
1+3	2+3	3+3	4+3	5+3	6+3	7+3			
1+2	2+2	3+2	4+2	5+2	6+2	7+2	8+2		
1+1	2+1	3+1	4+1	5+1	6+1	7+1	8+1	9+1	
1+0	2+0	3+0	4+0	5+0	6+0	7+0	8+0	9+0	10+0

Pick a subtraction card.

Find the related addition fact on the chart and shade it in.

Write the subtraction sentence and the shaded addition sentence.

Write the other two related facts.

Continue for at least 4 turns.

Lesson 39: Analyze the addition chart to create sets of related addition and subtraction facts.

185

Choose an expression card, and write 4 problems that use the same parts and totals. Shade the totals orange.

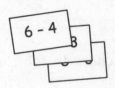

6 . 4 . 2
4 . 2 . 6
2 ⊕ 4 . 6
6 ⊖ 2 . 4

1. _____ − _____ = _____

_____ + _____ = _____

_____ ◯ _____ = _____

_____ ◯ _____ = _____

2. _____ − _____ = _____

_____ + _____ = _____

_____ ◯ _____ = _____

_____ ◯ _____ = _____

3. _____ − _____ = _____

_____ + _____ = _____

_____ ◯ _____ = _____

_____ ◯ _____ = _____

4. _____ − _____ = _____

_____ + _____ = _____

_____ ◯ _____ = _____

_____ ◯ _____ = _____

Lesson 39:   Analyze the addition chart to create sets of related addition and subtraction facts.

©2015 Great Minds. eureka-math.org
G1-M1-SE-B1-1.3.1-12.2015

EUREKA MATH

Name _____ Date _____

Solve the unshaded addition problems below.

1 + 0	1 + 1	1 + 2	1 + 3	1 + 4	1 + 5	1 + 6	1 + 7	1 + 8	1 + 9
2 + 0	2 + 1	2 + 2	2 + 3	2 + 4	2 + 5	2 + 6	2 + 7	2 + 8	
3 + 0	3 + 1	3 + 2	3 + 3	3 + 4	3 + 5	3 + 6	3 + 7		
4 + 0	4 + 1	4 + 2	4 + 3	4 + 4	4 + 5	4 + 6			
5 + 0	5 + 1	5 + 2	5 + 3	5 + 4	5 + 5				
6 + 0	6 + 1	6 + 2	6 + 3	6 + 4					
7 + 0	7 + 1	7 + 2	7 + 3						
8 + 0	8 + 1	8 + 2							
9 + 0	9 + 1								
10 + 0									

4 + 2

Pick an addition fact from the chart. Use the grid to write the two subtraction facts that would have the same number bond. Repeat in order to make a set of subtraction flash cards. To help you practice your addition and subtraction facts even more, make your own number bond flash cards with the templates on the last page.

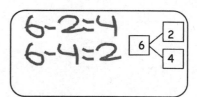

$6 - 2 = 4$
$6 - 4 = 2$

Lesson 39:   Analyze the addition chart to create sets of related addition and subtraction facts.

187

This page intentionally left blank

This page intentionally left blank

Lesson 39: Analyze the addition chart to create sets of related addition and subtraction facts.

189

©2015 Great Minds. eureka-math.org
G1-M1-SE-B1-1.3.1-12.2015

This page intentionally left blank

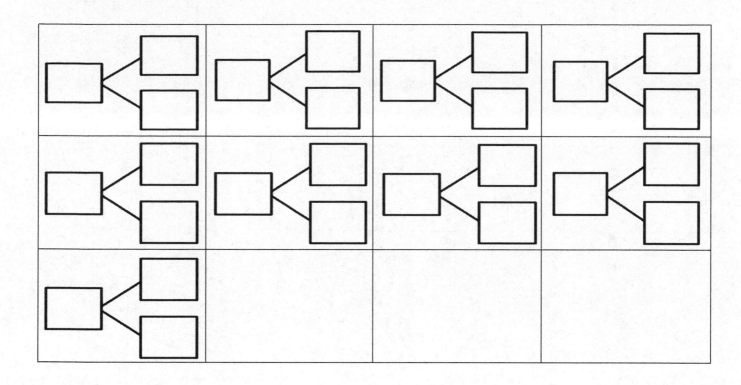

EUREKA MATH

Lesson 39:   Analyze the addition chart to create sets of related addition and
subtraction facts.

191

This page intentionally left blank

1+9									
1+8	2+8								
1+7	2+7	3+7							
1+6	2+6	3+6	4+6						
1+5	2+5	3+5	4+5	5+5					
1+4	2+4	3+4	4+4	5+4	6+4				
1+3	2+3	3+3	4+3	5+3	6+3	7+3			
1+2	2+2	3+2	4+2	5+2	6+2	7+2	8+2		
1+1	2+1	3+1	4+1	5+1	6+1	7+1	8+1	9+1	
1+0	2+0	3+0	4+0	5+0	6+0	7+0	8+0	9+0	10+0

_____

addition chart - from Lesson 21

Lesson 39:   Analyze the addition chart to create sets of related addition and subtraction facts.

193

This page intentionally left blank